THE ULTIMATE
LOS ANGELES KINGS
TRIVIA BOOK

A Collection of Amazing Trivia Quizzes
and Fun Facts for Die-Hard Kings Fans!

Ray Walker

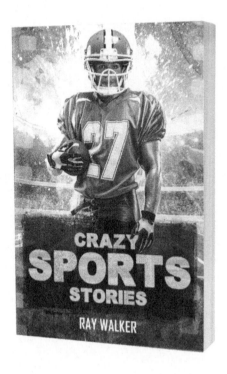

CONTENTS

INTRODUCTION

Many sports experts thought the National Hockey League was taking a huge risk by introducing hockey to the masses in California in 1967-68, but the Los Angeles Kings have proven them wrong. When the league doubled in size from 6 to 12 teams over 50 years ago, franchises were awarded to Oakland and Los Angeles. The Oakland Seals may be long gone, but the Los Angeles Kings are still going strong and have two Stanley Cup banners hanging from the rafters of the Staples Center.

With a loyal and passionate base of fans, the Kings have survived something of a rocky road along the way. Even after landing "The Great One," Wayne Gretzky, in the most surprising hockey trade ever in 1988, the organization came close to bankruptcy just seven years later. However, Philip Anschutz and Edward P. Roski saved the day by buying the franchise and putting it back on track.

Kings' fans have been treated to a very colorful history over the years. Who could forget Jack Kent Cooke, The Fabulous Forum, Eddie "The Entertainer" Shack, Marcel Dionne, Gretzky, Rogie Vachon, Luc Robitaille, Rob Blake, Bernie Nicholls, Drew Doughty, Anže Kopitar, and so many others?

Some of the sport's biggest stars and best coaches have worked their magic in LA and the future looks bright, even though the team has struggled lately.

This Los Angeles Kings trivia/fact book is filled with a wide range of information about the team from the day it was born to the conclusion of the 2019-20 regular NHL season. It features 15 different sections, each with 15 multiple-choice questions and five true-or-false statements. The answers are revealed on a separate page. Each chapter also offers 10 historical "Did You Know?" facts about the franchise's players, coaches, general managers, owners, etc.

Kings' supporters can refresh their memories with the book and relive the team's history, while maybe even learning something new at the same time. The book is an ideal way to prepare yourself for trivia challenges and contests with fellow L.A. fans.

Hopefully, Kings' fans will enjoy this historical journey, which is designed to remind them why they're such loyal fans of the team in the first place.

CHAPTER 1:

ORIGINS & HISTORY

QUIZ TIME!

1. Who was the Kings' first general manager?

    a. Red Kelly

    b. Jake Milford

    c. Larry Regan

    d. George Maguire

2. This person was the first owner of the Kings.

    a. Jack Kent Cooke

    b. Jerry Buss

    c. Joseph M. Cohen

    d. Jeffrey Sudikoff

3. The Los Angeles Kings got their name from a fan vote contest.

    a. True

    b. False

4. How much did it cost to bring the Kings to Los Angeles?

   a. $3 million

   b. $2 million

   c. $1.5 million

   d. $2.4 million

5. Where did the Kings play their home games for 32 seasons?

   a. Long Beach Arena

   b. Staples Center

   c. Los Angeles Memorial Arena

   d. The Forum

6. Which team did the Kings play their first NHL game against?

   a. Minnesota North Stars

   b. Philadelphia Flyers

   c. Chicago Blackhawks

   d. Detroit Red Wings

7. Who was the Kings' television play-by-play announcer for their first five seasons?

   a. Ed Fitkin

   b. Roy Storey

   c. Dan Avey

   d. Jiggs McDonald

8. Hal Laycoe was the King's first head coach.

   a. True

   b. False

9. When did the club make its first appearance in the Stanley Cup Final?

  a. 1992-93

  b. 1997-98

  c. 1995-96

  d. 1989-90

10. Which player did the team select first in the 1967 NHL expansion draft?

  a. Terry Sawchuk

  b. Wayne Rutledge

  c. Gord Labossiere

  d. Bob Wall

11. The Kings played the California Golden Seals in their first-ever playoff series.

  a. True

  b. False

12. How many times have the Kings made the playoffs as of 2018-19?

  a. 22

  b. 35

  c. 27

  d. 30

13. How many times have the Kings posted 100 or more points as of 2019-20?

  a. 2

  b. 6

c. 8

d. 5

14. The Kings franchise faced bankruptcy in 1995.

    a. True

    b. False

15. The squad spent how many seasons in the Norris Division?

    a. 5

    b. 6

    c. 7

    d. 8

16. Which player led the team with 57 points in their first season?

    a. Bill Flett

    b. Eddie Joyal

    c. Lowell McDonald

    d. Ted Irvine

17. How many coaches have the Kings had up to 2020?

    a. 19

    b. 26

    c. 18

    d. 23

18. What team handed the Kings their first NHL loss?

    a. St. Louis Blues

    b. Pittsburgh Penguins

    c. Toronto Maple Leafs

    d. Montreal Canadiens

19. How many people have served as general manager of the club as of 2020?

    a. 12

    b. 7

    c. 10

    d. 9

20. The Kings made the playoffs in their first three seasons.

    a. True

    b. False

QUIZ ANSWERS

1. C – Larry Regan

2. A – Jack Kent Cooke

3. A – True

4. B – $2 million

5. D – The Forum

6. B – Philadelphia Flyers

7. D – Jiggs McDonald

8. B – False

9. A – 1992-93

10. A – Terry Sawchuk

11. B – False

12. D – 30

13. D – 5

14. A – True

15. C – 7

16. B – Eddie Joyal

17. B – 26

18. C – Toronto Maple Leafs

19. D – 9

20. B – False

DID YOU KNOW?

1. The Los Angeles Kings NHL franchise is based in the city of Los Angeles, California, in the USA. The club made its NHL debut in 1967-68, when the league expanded from six to 12 teams, and it currently competes in the Pacific Division in the league's Western Conference. The Kings' minor league affiliate is the Ontario Reign of the American Hockey League (AHL).

2. The franchise was founded on June 5, 1967, after the city of Los Angeles was awarded a franchise in February 1966. The first owner of the club was Jack Kent Cooke. The Kings played their home games at the Forum in Inglewood and then moved to the Staples Center in the downtown area 32 years later in 1999.

3. Jack Kent Cooke was a Canadian entrepreneur who paid the NHL $2 million for an expansion franchise. Cooke held a fan contest to name the team and selected "Kings" because he felt it gave the club an air of royalty and represented leadership in hockey. He also chose the color scheme of gold and purple because those colors were traditionally associated with royalty.

4. Cook also owned the Los Angeles Lakers of the National Basketball Association, and the team wore the same colors as the Kings. Cooke wanted the Kings to play at the Los Angeles Memorial Sports Arena with the Lakers, but the

arena had already agreed to lease the building to the Los Angeles Blades of the Western Hockey League (WHL). Cooke then decided to build his own arena.

5. The Los Angeles Forum wasn't built in time for the start of the 1967-68 NHL campaign, so the team played several home games at the Long Beach Arena in the nearby community of Long Beach. The Kings' home opener took place on Oct. 14, 1967, with a 4–2 victory over the Philadelphia Flyers.

6. The Los Angeles Forum hosted its first Los Angeles Kings' game on Dec. 30, 1967, when the team was shut out 2-0 by the Philadelphia Flyers. The rink was also commonly known by its nickname "The Fabulous Forum."

7. The Kings made the playoffs in the first two seasons but then went through a postseason drought that ended in 1973-1974. In 1979, Dr. Jerry Buss bought the Los Angeles Kings, Los Angeles Lakers and the Forum from Jack Kent Cooke for $67.5 million. The rink then became known as The Great Western Forum.

8. Jerry Buss sold his controlling interest in the Los Angeles Kings to Bruce McNall in 1988 and McNall then traded for Wayne Gretzky to help revive the team's sagging attendance. He also changed the team's colors to silver and black.

9. Bruce McNall had financial difficulties and sold the Kings to Jeffrey Sudikoff and Joseph Cohen. However, Cohen and Sudikoff were soon forced into bankruptcy in 1995

and the franchise was then acquired by Philip Anschutz and Edward P. Roski for roughly $113 million. Anschutz owns the Anschutz Entertainment Group, which in turn operates the Staples Center. Roski and Anschutz still owned the Kings as of 2020.

10. The Kings made the Stanley Cup Final for the first time in 1992-93 but were beaten by Montreal in five games, with three losses coming in overtime. The Kings won their first Stanley Cup in 2011-12 when they beat New Jersey in six games and repeated as champions in 2013-14 when they downed the New York Rangers in five outings.

CHAPTER 2:

JERSEYS & NUMBERS

QUIZ TIME!

1. How many jersey numbers have the Kings retired as of 2020?

    a. 8
    b. 6
    c. 4
    d. 7

2. Who was the first player to wear No. 53 in 1994?

    a. Steve Heinze
    b. Jason Holland
    c. Teddy Purcell
    d. Brian McReynolds

3. The purple color the Kings originally wore was called "Forum blue."

    a. True
    b. False

4. When did the team change its colors to black and silver?

    a. 1989-90

    b. 1988-89

    c. 1991-92

    d. 1987-88

5. This player never wore No. 16.

    a. Eddie Joyal

    b. Bill Lesuk

    c. John Paul Kelly

    d. Marcel Dionne

6. How many players have worn the No. 10 as of 2019-20?

    a. 34

    b. 28

    c. 41

    d. 32

7. What color was the team's 50th-anniversary jersey?

    a. White

    b. Purple

    c. Silver

    d. Gold

8. Anže Kopitar wore No. 60 in his first season with the Kings.

    a. True

    b. False

9. What was the crest on the Kings' first alternate jersey that only lasted the 1995-96 season?

   a. King's head wearing a crown
   b. Sword and shield
   c. Knight on a horse
   d. A castle

10. Which number did Justin Williams wear from 2009 to 2015?

    a. 13
    b. 11
    c. 15
    d. 14

11. Jarome Iginla wore No. 12 for the club.

    a. True
    b. False

12. Tanner Pearson was the first player in team history to wear which number?

    a. 33
    b. 50
    c. 70
    d. 85

13. Which player has worn No. 23 from 2004 to 2019-20?

    a. Jarret Stoll
    b. Alec Martinez
    c. Dustin Brown
    d. Trevor Lewis

14. The team reintroduced a crown as its primary logo in 1999-00.

    a. True
    b. False

15. Goalie Rogatien Vachon wore what number with the Kings?

    a. 30
    b. 1
    c. 31
    d. 25

16. Who wore No. 22 from 1985 to 1988?

    a. Brian Wilks
    b. Jimmy Carson
    c. Jay Wells
    d. Tiger Williams

17. How many different primary logos have the Kings had as of 2019-20?

    a. 3
    b. 4
    c. 6
    d. 5

18. This player was the first to wear No. 97 in 2005-06.

    a. John Zeiler
    b. Martin Straka
    c. Jeremy Roenick
    d. Ken Belanger

19. Who wore No. 17 from 1992-96?

    a. Matt Johnson

    b. Jari Kurri

    c. John Druce

    d. Mattias Norström

20. The Kings have worn 6 special event jerseys.

    a. True

    b. False

QUIZ ANSWERS

1. B – 6

2. D – Brian McReynolds

3. A – True

4. B – 1988-89

5. C – John Paul Kelly

6. D – 32

7. C – Silver

8. B – False

9. A – King's head wearing a crown

10. D – 14

11. B – False

12. C – 70

13. C – Dustin Brown

14. B – False

15. A – 30

16. D – Tiger Williams

17. D – 5

18. C – Jeremy Roenick

19. B – Jari Kurri

20. A – True

DID YOU KNOW?

1. The Kings' home jersey is predominantly black with silver and white trim while the away jersey is mainly white with silver and black trim. There is also an alternate jersey that is predominantly silver with black trim. The club wears black pants with each jersey and the socks worn are the same color as whichever jersey is being worn.

2. The team's original colors were primarily purple with gold trim; the purple was named "Forum blue." The pants were also Forum blue but gold pants were worn with the predominantly gold jerseys in the 1970s. The uniforms were modified between 1980 and 1988 and white trim was also added.

3. When Bruce McNall took over as franchise owner in 1988 and Wayne Gretzky was acquired, the team's color scheme changed dramatically to black and silver, much like the Los Angeles Raiders NFL team. In addition, a new primary logo was introduced. These uniforms were worn until 1997-98.

4. The Kings added back some purple and gold accents in 1995-96, when they came up with an alternate jersey that featured a medieval-type serif text with a logo of a bearded person wearing a golden crown. This jersey was commonly known as the "Burger King" jersey and was put to sleep after just one season because the team's fans weren't too thrilled with it.

5. New logos and uniforms were also introduced in the 1998–99 season, featuring a purple-silver-white color scheme that was similar to the Sacramento Kings of the NBA. One reason for this was that black and silver had suddenly become associated with the colors of certain Los Angeles area street gangs. The primary logo consisted of a crest and shield with three royal symbols: a lion wearing sunglasses, the sun and a crown. Also, the city's name was written on the bottom of the jersey.

6. The club also introduced an alternate purple jersey in 1999–2000 with an updated crown logo that would become the primary logo in 2002. Another alternate jersey came in 2008 with an updated logo and the letters "LA" added. The purple road jerseys were worn until 2010–11, while the home jersey became the alternate option in 2011 and was won until 2013.

7. The team has worn classic throwback jerseys for special events such as "Legends Night," NHL Stadium Series games, and their 50th anniversary season in 2016-17. Starting in the 2018-19 campaign, the club brought back its alternate silver uniforms, which were last worn in 2016-17, with minor modifications. The squad also wore its 1992-98 white jerseys for select games in 2019-20 as well as a new 2020 NHL Stadium Series uniform.

8. Six jersey numbers have been retired by the franchise. These are 4 (Rob Blake), 16 (Marcel Dionne), 18 (Dave Taylor), 20 (Luc Robitaille), 30 (Rogatien Vachon) and 99

(Wayne Gretzky). Even though Gretzky played for the Kings between 1988 and 1996, the NHL retired his No. 99 league-wide at the league's 2000 All-Star Game. The Kings also retired it in a ceremony in October 2002.

9. As of 2019-20, the most popular jersey numbers with Kings' players over the years have been 10 and 12, as 32 different players have donned those numbers. Coming a close second is No. 14, which was the choice of 30 different skaters.

10. Every number from 1 to 58 has been worn by at least one Kings player. In addition, 24 numbers between 61 and 99 have been worn. As for the No. 13 jersey, which is regarded as back luck in some cultures, four different players have been brave enough to tempt fate. They were Robert Lang (1992-96), Mike Cammalleri (2003-08), John Zeiler (2008-09) and Kyle Clifford (2010-20).

CHAPTER 3:

FAMOUS QUOTES

QUIZ TIME!

1. Which former Kings center was known to say, "Never let anyone steal your joy"?

    a. Mike Richards

    b. Marcel Dionne

    c. Bernie Nicholls

    d. Wayne Gretzky

2. Which Hall-of-Famer did this quote originate from? "I kind of have to pinch myself. A lot of my dreams are coming true."

    a. Larry Murphy

    b. Jarome Iginla

    c. Rob Blake

    d. Jari Kurri

3. Jeff Carter responded to a quote of his being taken out of context as follows, "Out in Vancouver, guys twisted my words. Ticking me off. I just want to go play and win games."

a. True

b. False

4. "Optional is Latin for 'be there,'" was said by which head coach, referring to the team's next practice?

    a. Red Kelly

    b. Tom Webster

    c. Marc Crawford

    d. Darryl Sutter

5. This head coach stated, "Maybe one of the qualities of being a great coach is being a jerk. There are quite a few of them around."

    a. Mike Murphy

    b. Pat Quinn

    c. Larry Robinson

    d. Barry Melrose

6. Which former King remarked, "I told Kopitar 'You aren't touching the puck enough. I don't like your breakout.' I think Kopitar can make magic with the puck"?

    a. Warren Rychel

    b. Charlie Simmer

    c. Marcel Dionne

    d. Jim Thomson

7. Which center remarked, "I missed 100 percent of the shots I didn't take"?

    a. Tyler Toffoli

    b. Anže Kopitar

    c. Wayne Gretzky

    d. Vincent Lecavalier

8. Reflecting on Wayne Gretzky's 802nd goal, Luc Robitaille said, "I don't know why no one's asked me for my stick? But I still have it."

    a. True

    b. False

9. "I didn't have all the expectations and publicity. It probably made me work harder and learn more. It was a blessing in disguise," was said by this player.

    a. Dustin Penner

    b. Bill Lesuk

    c. Dean Kennedy

    d. Jim Fox

10. Which member of the front office once claimed, "At the end of each year I make a list of my mistakes and it's pretty frigging long"?

    a. Bruce McCall

    b. Dean Lombardi

    c. George Maguire

    d. Sam McMaster

11. Jonathan Quick complimented goalie Cal Petersen's play with this comment, "Since he's been up he's played great for us and last year when he was up he did that as well."

    a. True

    b. False

12. "This ain't gonna be no oil painting," was said by which coach before an upcoming game?

   a. Barry Melrose
   b. Bob Pulford
   c. Darryl Sutter
   d. Roger Neilson

13. When asked if it was easier to make saves in overtime this goalie answered, "No it's tough. They've got some good players on the ice."

   a. Jonathan Quick
   b. Jack Campbell
   c. Ben Scrivens
   d. Martin Jones

14. After enduring a Kings' losing streak, Jari Kurri once said "I wish I was still in Edmonton."

   a. True
   b. False

15. After losing the first three playoff games to Vegas in 2018, who said, "We trust in ourselves. It's been done before … and we can definitely do it. Just got to believe and trust in each other."

   a. Alex Iafallo
   b. Drew Doughty
   c. Dustin Brown
   d. Tanner Pearson

16. Following a loss to Vancouver in October 2019, who stated, "A team like that should not be beating a team like ours 8-2. Absolutely no way"?

    a. Head coach Todd McLellan
    b. Anže Kopitar
    c. Sean Walker
    d. Drew Doughty

17. Who was San Jose's Bernie Nicholls referring to when he said "You're always aware of him physically. ... He's the best we play against"?

    a. Matt Johnson
    b. Sean O'Donnell
    c. Kevin Stevens
    d. Rob Blake

18. "We'd look at the other team's lineup and think let's have a good time and not lose by too much," was said by who in the 1990s?

    a. Ray Ferraro
    b. Roman Vopat
    c. Doug Zmolek
    d. Rob Blake

19. "It's easier to lose than it is to win," was a quote by this King.

    a. Ian Turnbull
    b. Paul Fenton
    c. Jerry Korab
    d. Wayne Gretzky

20. Marcel Dionne had this to say about never winning the Stanley Cup, "Winning the series against the Soviet Union was the best. It was the greatest experience of my hockey career by far."

    a. True
    b. False

QUIZ ANSWERS

1. A – Mike Richards

2. B – Jarome Iginla

3. B – False

4. D – Darryl Sutter

5. C – Larry Robinson

6. C – Marcel Dionne

7. C – Wayne Gretzky

8. A – True

9. A – Dustin Penner

10. B – Dean Lombardi

11. A – True

12. A – Barry Melrose

13. A – Jonathan Quick

14. B – False

15. A – Alex Iafallo

16. D – Drew Doughty

17. D – Rob Blake

18. D – Rob Blake

19. D – Wayne Gretzky

20. A-True

DID YOU KNOW?

1. Former Kings' winger Jarome Iginla once said, "I want to be the top player in the league and I want to bring my game to another level. I want to play against the opposition's best players—and I want to beat them." Iginla definitely took his game to another level, as he was inducted into the Hockey Hall of Fame in 2020.

2. "A complacent player is a lazy player, and a lazy player is a loser." This was said by former head coach Darryl Sutter after being asked his views on players becoming complacent. Sutter might know as he won a pair of Stanley Cups with the team.

3. When speaking about one of his NHL counterparts, former Los Angeles head coach Marc Crawford remarked, "Mike Keenan has been responsible for creating a lot of good things for coaches, like mid-season job openings."

4. Hall-of-Fame blue-liner Larry Robinson, who played for and coached the Kings, had this to say about one of his biggest rivals: "I don't think you ever stopped Bobby Orr. You contained Bobby Orr, but you never stopped him. When we played the Bruins and Bobby had to give up the puck, it was a good play."

5. Asked if he had any regrets about playing in Los Angeles, Marcel Dionne came up with this gem: "I had an opportunity many, many times to go to the Playboy

Mansion with Hugh Hefner. Jerry Buss asked me many times and you know what, looking back that was stupid of me not going there."

6. It would be hard to criticize Wayne Gretzky's work ethic since he's the NHL's all-time top scorer and arguably best-ever player. He once said, "The highest compliment that you can pay me is to say that I work hard every day, that I never dog it."

7. When speaking about being benched during a game, former Kings' forward Dustin Penner once claimed, "The guillotine has to fall somewhere when the team under-produces, and more times than not it's fallen on me."

8. When the NHL started adding fractions of a second to the time clock, former GM Dean Lombardi described it this way, "Those clocks are sophisticated instruments that calculate time by measuring electrical charges—given the rapidity and volume of electrons that move through the device the calibrator must adjust at certain points which was the delay you see—the delay is just re-calibrating for the clock moving too quickly during the 10ths of a second before the delay—this insures the period is exactly 20 minutes. That is not an opinion—that is science."

9. After falling behind 2-0 in a playoff series against the Vegas Golden Knights, goaltender Jonathan Quick's opinion was, "It's a new game. If we're up 2-0, if we're down 2-0, it don't matter. We're just trying to win a hockey game in Game 3. They're doing the same thing so,

if you're trying to pull positives, you're in trouble if you're looking for that. We're just trying to win a hockey game like anyone else."

10. After the NHL closed shop for several months due to COVID-19 in 2020, Drew Doughty commented, "I just miss seeing the guys. ... Some of the best parts of hockey are just being in the locker room with the guys. ... Going to the room, looking forward to just laughing the whole time, hearing stories from the young guys, and the old guys about their kids or whatever it may be."

CHAPTER 4:

CATCHY NICKNAMES

QUIZ TIME!

1. What nickname did Marcel Dionne have?

    a. Gopher

    b. Junior

    c. Hot Sauce

    d. Little Beaver

2. Who was given the nickname "Doughnut"?

    a. Rogatien Vachon

    b. Drew Doughty

    c. Dave Taylor

    d. Dustin Brown

3. Wayne Gretzky is known as "Mighty Fine 99."

    a. True

    b. False

4. What is Jonathan Quick's nickname?

    a. Wallsey

    b. Quicker

c. Quicksy

d. Bricks

5. Who was known as "Hollywood"?

   a. Rob Blake

   b. Bernie Nicholls

   c. Kelly Hrudey

   d. Luc Robitaille

6. Jeff Carter is called what by his teammates?

   a. Cartsy

   b. Car

   c. J.C.

   d. Carts

7. Which player was known as "Pumper"?

   a. Tom Laidlaw

   b. Steve Kasper

   c. Bernie Nicholls

   d. John Tonelli

8. Jari Kurri was dubbed "Lucky" by teammates.

   a. True

   b. False

9. Which is not one of former Kings player Kyle Clifford's nicknames?

   a. Rocky

   b. Colonel

   c. Cliffy

   d. Big Red Dog

10. Kings goalie Grant Fuhr had which moniker?

    a. Grand Grant
    b. Furious Fuhr
    c. The Count
    d. Coco

11. Steve Kasper was called "Ghost."

    a. True
    b. False

12. What is Anže Kopitar's nickname?

    a. Kops
    b. Kopi
    c. Star
    d. Annie

13. Which Kings' player was known as "Pony"?

    a. Jean Potvin
    b. Ziggy Pálffy
    c. Bryan Smolinski
    d. Alexei Ponikarovsky

14. Rob Brown was called "the Bowman" while playing for the Kings.

    a. True
    b. False

15. Wayne Simmonds was given which nickname in Los Angeles?

    a. Salt
    b. Nails

c. Simmer

d. Hustle

16. Which goaltender was nicknamed "Soupy"?

    a. Jack Campbell

    b. Bob Janecyk

    c. Jonathan Bernier

    d. Stéphane Fiset

17. Justin Williams was given this nickname with the Kings.

    a. Stick

    b. Willis

    c. Half-stack

    d. Willie

18. Sean Avery was known by this nickname.

    a. Savory

    b. Bull Dog

    c. Savvy Av

    d. The Rat

19. Who was known as "Zeus"?

    a. Brian Boyle

    b. Matt Moulson

    c. Michal Handzuš

    d. Teddy Purcell

20. Tyler Toffoli's nickname was "Tofu."

    a. True

    b. False

QUIZ ANSWERS

1. D – Little Beaver

2. B – Drew Doughty

3. B – False

4. B – Quicker

5. C – Kelly Hrudey

6. D – Carts

7. C – Bernie Nicholls

8. B – False

9. A – Rocky

10. D – Coco

11. B – False

12. B – Kopi

13. D – Alexei Ponikarovsky

14. B – False

15. C – Simmer

16. A – Jack Campbell

17. A – Stick

18. D – The Rat

19. C – Michal Handzuš

20. B – False

DID YOU KNOW

1. The city of Los Angeles is simply nicknamed LA and is also known as "The City of Angels," "La-La Land," "City of Flowers and Sunshine," "Lost Angeles," Lotusland," "Southland," and "Tinseltown." The official nickname for the state of California is "The Golden State." However, the hockey club is simply known as "The Kings" or "LA."

2. The Kings' first owner, Jack Kent Cooke, often nicknamed his players in the early years. He reportedly came up with these monikers: Juha "Whitey" Widing, Eddie "The Jet" Joyal, Bill "Cowboy" Flett, Eddie "The Entertainer" Shack, and Real "Frenchy" Lemieux.

3. The famous "Triple Crown Line" of the Kings consisted of wingers Dave Taylor and Charlie Simmer, centered by Marcel Dionne. The trio played together from 1979 to 1984 and, in the 1980-81 season, they combined for 352 points. This made it the first line in the history of the NHL in which each member tallied 100 or more points in the same season.

4. Center Marcel Dionne also had his own nickname, "The Little Beaver." Legend has it that Dionne earned the moniker since he resembled a short professional wrestler who used the name. Dionne was the third-highest scorer in NHL history when he retired.

5. Since he went to an Ivy League college in America, former

Kings' netminder Ben Scrivens was known as "The Professor." He played with the team in 2013-14 and went 7-5-4 with a remarkable 1.97 goals-against average, .931 save percentage, and 3 shutouts in 19 games. His wife, Jenny Scrivens, was also a professional hockey goalie who played in the National Women's Hockey League (NWHL).

6. Former King Martin Jones had a figurine of him marketed as "Game of Jones," after the television program *The Game of Thrones*. The undrafted goaltender spent several seasons in the minors before making his NHL debut in 2013 and he played 34 regular-season games with the Kings. The restricted free agent was then traded to San Jose two weeks after the Kings dealt him to Boston.

7. Former blue-liner and head coach Larry Robinson was known affectionately by fans and teammates as "Big Bird." Robinson stood 6-feet-4-inches tall, weighed 225 pounds, and was named after the Big Bird character from the television show *Sesame Street*. Robinson played the last three seasons of his career in LA and then coached the club for four full seasons between 1995 and 1999.

8. High-scoring center Bernie Nicholls was drafted 73rd overall by LA in 1980 and soon earned the nickname "The Pumper Nicholl Kid," after pumpernickel bread. Nicholls played with the team from 1981-82 to 1989-90 before being traded to the New York Rangers in a controversial blockbuster deal.

9. Forward Dustin Penner arrived in LA in February 2011 in a trade with Edmonton. A year later, he suffered back spasms

while eating pancakes and was forced to miss a game due to the discomfort. From then on, Penner's nickname became "Pancakes." Penner notched the overtime winner against Phoenix in Game 5 of the conference finals to send the Kings to the 2012 Stanley Cup Final.

10. The Kings acquired Felix Potvin in 2000-01 from Vancouver. The goaltender was known as "The Cat" after the cartoon character Felix the Cat because of his cat-like reflexes. He went 13-5-5 immediately after joining the team with a 1.96 goals-against average and a .919 save percentage. "The Cat" then helped the Kings eliminate Detroit in the first round of the playoffs and pushed the eventual Stanley Cup Champion Colorado to seven games with consecutive shutouts in the series.

CHAPTER 5:

THE CAPTAIN CLASS

QUIZ TIME!

1. Who was LA's first captain?

    a. Bill White

    b. Larry Cahan

    c. Bob Wall

    d. Eddie Joyal

2. This player was the club's longest-serving captain at eight seasons.

    a. Dustin Brown

    b. Wayne Gretzky

    c. Mike Murphy

    d. Rob Blake

3. Larry Cahan was the oldest captain of the team at the age of 38.

    a. True

    b. False

4. Which player has the most goals in a season while serving as team captain?

   a. Wayne Gretzky
   b. Dave Taylor
   c. Luc Robitaille
   d. Anže Kopitar

5. What is the record for the most penalty minutes in a season for a team captain?

   a. 128
   b. 130
   c. 129
   d. 144

6. Which Hall-of-Famer wore the "C" in 1971-72?

   a. Billy Smith
   b. Dick Duff
   c. Harry Howell
   d. Bob Pulford

7. How many seasons was Mattias Norström captain of the Kings?

   a. 3
   b. 5
   c. 4
   d. 6

8. Jeff Carter and Drew Doughty have been alternate captains since 2016-17.

   a. True
   b. False

9. This captain posted the best plus/minus in a season at +38.

    a. Mike Murphy
    b. Luc Robitaille
    c. Terry Harper
    d. Anže Kopitar

10. Dustin Brown became the youngest captain of the squad in 2008 at what age?

    a. 25
    b. 24
    c. 23
    d. 26

11. As of 2019-20, five former captains have been inducted into the Hockey Hall of Fame.

    a. True
    b. False

12. The most assists recorded by a captain in a season is?

    a. 66
    b. 107
    c. 92
    d. 122

13. How many players have served as captain as of 2019-20?

    a. 14
    b. 15
    c. 12
    d. 16

14. The lowest plus/minus recorded by a captain was -43 in 1969-70.

    a. True
    b. False

15. Which season did Luc Robitaille hold the captaincy for a brief period?

    a. 1991-92
    b. 1992-93
    c. 1993-94
    d. 1994-95

16. Who was captain from 1981 to 1983?

    a. Bernie Nicholls
    b. Marcel Dionne
    c. Terry Ruskowski
    d. Dave Lewis

17. How old was Anže Kopitar when was named captain in June 2016?

    a. 28
    b. 30
    c. 29
    d. 27

18. The fewest goals scored by a captain in a season with a minimum of 70 games played is?

    a. 3
    b. 2
    c. 1
    d. 0

19. How many points did Bob Pulford tally in his lone season as captain?

    a. 40
    b. 37
    c. 28
    d. 19

20. Marcel Dionne never served as the Kings' skipper.

    a. True
    b. False

QUIZ ANSWERS

1. C – Bob Wall

2. A – Dustin Brown

3. B – False

4. A – Wayne Gretzky

5. D – 144

6. D – Bob Pulford

7. B – 5

8. A – True

9. C – Terry Harper

10. C – 23

11. B – False

12. D – 122

13. A – 14

14. A – True

15. B – 1992-93

16. D – Dave Lewis

17. A – 28

18. D – 0

19. B – 37

20. A – True

DID YOU KNOW?

1. The Kings have had 14 different players act as captain since entering the NHL. Bob Wall was the first, followed by Larry Cahan, Bob Pulford, Terry Harper, Mike Murphy, Dave Lewis, Terry Ruskowski, Dave Taylor, Wayne Gretzky, Luc Robitaille, Rob Blake, Mattias Norström, Dustin Brown, and the latest skipper, Anže Kopitar, who was appointed in 2016.

2. Winger Luc Robitaille and Wayne Gretzky both acted as captain in 1992-93, when Gretzky played just 45 regular-season games due to injury. Rob Blake took over the "C" in 1996 after Gretzky was dealt to St. Louis at the trade deadline. Blake was traded to Colorado in 2001 and was renamed captain for 2007-08 when he returned to the Kings, taking over from Mattias Norström.

3. Mattias Norström was one of the Kings' low-key captains as he was basically a low-scoring defenseman. He was acquired by LA in March 1996 in a multi-player deal with the New York Rangers and stayed until being traded to Dallas in February 2007 in another multi-player deal. Norström played 780 regular-season games with the Kings and posted 142 points, with 583 penalty minutes.

4. There was no official captain of the Kings for the 1972-73 season when Juha Widing, Ralph Backstrom, and Harry Howell acted as alternate captains. The previous captain

was Bob Pulford. However, he retired just before the season began to take over as the team's head coach.

5. The youngest captain in Kings' history has been Dustin Brown, who was a month shy of his 24th birthday when taking the job in October 2008. The oldest skipper so far was Rob Blake, who was 38 years old when wearing the "C" in 2007-08.

6. Physical winger Dustin Brown was captain for both Stanley Cup triumphs. He was drafted 13th overall by the Kings in 2003 and, at the conclusion of the 2019-20 regular season, he had accumulated 299 goals and 653 points in 1,183 games, with 700 penalty minutes. He also had 47 points in 85 playoff outings, with 84 penalty minutes. Brown was replaced as captain by Anže Kopitar in June 2016.

7. It's no surprise to hear that Wayne Gretzky registered the highest-scoring season as a Kings' captain. In fact, he had the top three seasons in points. "The Great One" posted 163 points in 1990-91, 142 points in 1989-90, and 130 points in 1993-94. He also notched 121 points in 1991-92. The only other captain to break the 100-point barrier was Luc Robitaille, with 125 points in 1992-93, when he set a club-high for captains in goals with 63.

8. Terry Ruskowski was a grinder who brought a physical presence to the ice. He served the most penalty minutes in a season as LA captain with 144 minutes in 78 games in 1984-85. He also chipped in with 16 goals and 49 points.

Ruskowski had excellent leadership abilities and he's reportedly the only hockey player to captain four pro teams; he was skipper of the Kings, Pittsburgh Penguins and Chicago Blackhawks of the NHL and the Houston Aeros of the WHA.

9. The Kings' first captain was blue-liner Bob Wall, who wore the "C" for the first two seasons. Wall was claimed from Detroit in the 1967 NHL expansion draft. He played 212 regular-season games for LA with 23 goals and 67 points before being traded to St. Louis in May 1970.

10. Two former Kings captains went on to become head coach of the team. Bob Pulford was skipper in 1971-72 and then took over behind the bench from 1972-73 to the end of the 1976-77 season. Fellow forward Mike Murphy captained the team for six full seasons from 1975 to 1981 and coached the club for 65 games between 1986-87 and 1987-88.

CHAPTER 6:

STATISTICALLY SPEAKING

QUIZ TIME!

1. What is the franchise record for most goals scored in the regular season by a player?

    a. 59

    b. 63

    c. 66

    d. 70

2. Who earned the most assists in a season?

    a. Luc Robitaille

    b. Wayne Gretzky

    c. Marcel Dionne

    d. Bernie Nicholls

3. The Kings recorded 72 points in their first season.

    a. True

    b. False

4. The team set a franchise record for most losses in a season in 1969-70 with how many?

    a. 52
    b. 45
    c. 47
    d. 50

5. Who leads the team in career, regular-season power play goals?

    a. Dustin Brown
    b. Jimmy Carson
    c. Charlie Simmer
    d. Luc Robitaille

6. What is the record for most points by the Kings in a season?

    a. 102
    b. 104
    c. 105
    d. 108

7. This goaltender has played over 37,000 minutes in his career with the Kings.

    a. Rogatien Vachon
    b. Jonathan Quick
    c. Mario Lessard
    d. Kelly Hrudey

8. Bernie Nicholls averaged 0.89 goals per game in 1988-89.

    a. True
    b. False

9. Who recorded the most penalty minutes in a season for the Kings?

    a. Tiger Williams
    b. Marty McSorley
    c. Warren Rychel
    d. Sean Avery

10. What is the record for most game-winning goals by a player in a single season?

    a. 12
    b. 8
    c. 10
    d. 9

11. Jimmy Carson has scored the most hat tricks in a single season.

    a. True
    b. False

12. How many goals did the Kings notch in their first season?

    a. 213
    b. 206
    c. 224
    d. 200

13. What is the lowest number of points the Kings have recorded in a season?

    a. 41
    b. 49
    c. 54
    d. 38

14. Jonathan Quick earned 5 assists in 2017-18.

    a. True

    b. False

15. Which coach leads the club in regular-season wins?

    a. Terry Murray

    b. Bob Pulford

    c. Darryl Sutter

    d. Andy Murray

16. What is the record for the most wins by the Kings in a season?

    a. 48

    b. 52

    c. 49

    d. 50

17. What is the record for most regular-season losses in a season for a Kings goalie?

    a. 29

    b. 28

    c. 31

    d. 34

18. Who had a shooting percentage of 32.7 in 1980-81?

    a. Dave Taylor

    b. Charlie Simmer

    c. Jim Fox

    d. Dan Bonar

19. How many goals did the Kings score in the playoffs to win their first Stanley Cup?

   a. 52
   b. 39
   c. 45
   d. 57

20. Rob Blake has attempted the most shots on goal in a single season for the Kings.

   a. True
   b. False

QUIZ ANSWERS

1. D – 70

2. B – Wayne Gretzky

3. A – True

4. A – 52

5. D – Luc Robitaille

6. C – 105

7. B – Jonathan Quick

8. A – True

9. B – Marty McSorley

10. C – 10

11. A – True

12. D – 200

13. D – 38

14. B – False

15. C – Darryl Sutter

16. A – 48

17. C – 31

18. B – Charlie Simmer

19. D – 57

20. B – False

DID YOU KNOW?

1. When the 2019-20 NHL regular-season officially came to an end, the Kings possessed an all-time (won-lost-tied-overtime/shootout losses) record of 1733-1800-424-159 for 4,049 points. The club was also 111-144 in the playoffs and had made the postseason 30 times as of 2020.

2. The most points the Kings earned in a season was the 105 they posted in 1974-75, when they had a record of 42-17-21. The fewest points scored, 38, came in 1969-70 with a mark of 14-52-10. Their best points percentage was .656, also in 1974-75, and the 1969-70 season was their lowest at .250.

3. The all-time points and assists leader for LA is Marcel Dionne, who racked up 1,307 and 757 respectively. Luc Robitaille leads in goals with 557 while Dustin Brown had played the most regular-season games by the conclusion of 2019-20 at 1,183. Marty McSorley accumulated the most regular-season penalty minutes with 1,846 and Dave Taylor owns the best career plus/minus at +186.

4. Marcel Dionne is also tops in regular-season even-strength goals with 369, while Luc Robitaille is the career leader in power play markers at 210 and game-winners with 73. Bernie Nicholls was the greatest threat when down a man as he tallied 25 shorthanded goals. The most accurate Kings' shooter was Charlie Simmer at 23 percent.

5. On a career, per-game basis for the organization, Marcel Dionne scored .60 goals per game while Wayne Gretzky earned 1.25 assists and 1.70 points per game. Gretzky also holds the team records for assists and points per game in a single season at 1.56 and 2.15. Meanwhile, Bernie Nicholls tallied the most goals per game in a campaign at 0.89.

6. Other franchise single-season records include Bernie Nicholls with 70 goals, 41 even-strength goals, 8 shorthanded markers, and 385 shots on net; Wayne Gretzky with 122 assists and 168 points; Marcel Dionne with a +54 rating; Marty McSorley with 399 penalty minutes; Luc Robitaille with 26 power-play goals, Charlie Simmer with 10 game-winners and a 32.7 shooting percentage; Jimmy Carson with 5 hat tricks.

7. When it comes to career, regular-season goaltending, Jonathan Quick led the way in games played (644) by the end of 2019-20 as well as wins (325), losses (240), ties/overtime/shootout losses (67), goals-against (1,499), shots against (17,312), saves (15,813) minutes (37,612) and shutouts (52). He was also tops in save percentage (.913) and goals-against average (2.39) for goalies with over 200 games.

8. Kings' single-season goaltending records at the end of 2019-20 were: Jonathan Quick for games played (72), wins (40), save percentage (.929), and goals-against average (1.95) in over 50 games played, shutouts (10) and minutes (4,258). He also co-shared the mark for ties/overtime/shootout

losses (13) with Kelly Hrudey and Rogatien Vachon. Hrudey also led the way in losses (31), goals-against (228), shots against (2,219), and saves (1,991).

9. Where the postseason is concerned, Luc Robitaille has played the most games at 94, scored the most goals with 41, tallied a team-high 14 power-play markers, and had 9 game-winning goals. Wayne Gretzky notched 65 assists and 94 points and is tied with Dustin Brown, Anže Kopitar, Jari Kurri and Dave Taylor at 2 shorthanded goals. Marty McSorley registered the most penalty minutes at 190.

10. In playoff goaltending, Jonathan Quick leads across the board as he has played 85 games with a team-best 2.23 goals-against and .923 save percentage for goalies who played at least 7 games, with 46 wins, 39 losses, and 9 shutouts.

CHAPTER 7:

THE TRADE MARKET

QUIZ TIME!

1. How many 1st-round draft picks were sent to Edmonton in the trade for Wayne Gretzky?

   a. 4

   b. 3

   c. 5

   d. 2

2. Which player did the Kings NOT receive from the New York Rangers in exchange for Barclay Plager?

   a. Jim Murray

   b. Ken Turlik

   c. Gerry Desjardins

   d. Trevor Fahey

3. On June 8, 1967, the Kings made their first-ever trade, sending Ken Block to Toronto for the rights to Red Kelly.

   a. True

   b. False

4. Who did the Kings receive for Patrick O'Sullivan in 2008-09?

    a. Richard Clune and Jarret Stoll
    b. Sean O'Donnell
    c. Justin Williams
    d. Jarret Stoll and Matt Greene

5. In 2011-12, the Kings traded which player and a first-round pick to Columbus for Jeff Carter?

    a. Kevin Westgarth
    b. Wayne Simmonds
    c. Jack Johnson
    d. Ryan Smyth

6. How many trades did Los Angeles make in 2003-04?

    a. 12
    b. 8
    c. 14
    d. 9

7. What was not part of the trade package Toronto sent to LA for Jake Muzzin in 2018-19?

    a. Sean Durzi
    b. 2019 3rd-round draft pick
    c. Carl Grundstrom
    d. 2019 1st-round draft pick

8. Alan May and Jim Wiemer were not part of the 1988 Wayne Gretzky trade.

    a. True
    b. False

9. The Kings traded Tyler Toffoli to Vancouver for which two players?

   a. Trevor Moore and Tim Schaller
   b. Tim Schaller and Tyler Madden
   c. Pavel Jenyš and Trevor Moore
   d. Peter Budaj and Tyler Madden

10. From what team did the Kings acquire goalie Grant Fuhr in 1994-95?

   a. Toronto Maple Leafs
   b. Calgary Flames
   c. St. Louis Blues
   d. Buffalo Sabres

11. The Kings traded Rob Blake and Steve Reinprecht to Colorado in 2000-01.

   a. True
   b. False

12. The Kings traded Tiger Williams to the Hartford Whalers for?

   a. Gord Walker
   b. A 4th-round draft pick
   c. Cash
   d. Future considerations

13. Who did LA send to the New York Islanders on March 10, 1980?

   a. Garry Unger
   b. Dave Hutchinson

c. Butch Goring

d. Ian Turnbull

14. The Kings traded a 1st-round draft pick for goalie Dan Cloutier.

    a. True

    b. False

15. Which team did the Kings make four trades with in 1969-70?

    a. St. Louis Blues

    b. Oakland Seals

    c. Boston Bruins

    d. Montreal Canadiens

16. Who did the Kings receive from Pittsburgh for Luc Robitaille in 1994-95?

    a. Eric Lacroix and Chris Snell

    b. Rick Tocchet

    c. Arto Blomsten

    d. Randy Burridge

17. Who was sent to LA by Philadelphia for Wayne Simmonds and Brayden Schenn in 2011-12?

    a. Rob Bordson and Mike Richards

    b. Colin Fraser and Marco Sturm

    c. Mike Richards and Colin Fraser

    d. Rob Bordson and Marco Sturm

18. How many players were involved in a trade between the Kings and New York Rangers on March 14, 1996?

a. 9

b. 10

c. 7

d. 8

19. The Kings did not acquire this player for Wayne Gretzky from St. Louis Blues on Feb. 27, 1996.

    a. Patrice Tardif

    b. Roman Vopat

    c. Craig Johnson

    d. Doug Zmolek

20. LA traded goalies Ben Bishop and Darcy Kuemper in the 2016-17 season.

    a. True

    b. False

QUIZ ANSWERS

1. B – 3

2. C – Gerry Desjardins

3. A – True

4. C – Justin Williams

5. C – Jack Johnson

6. B – 8

7. B – 2019 3rd-round draft pick

8. A – True

9. B – Tim Schaller and Tyler Madden

10. D – Buffalo Sabres

11. A – True

12. C – Cash

13. C – Butch Goring

14. B – False

15. D – Montreal Canadiens

16. B – Rick Tocchet

17. A – Rob Bordson and Mike Richards

18. C – 7

19. D – Doug Zmolek

20. B – False

DID YOU KNOW?

1. In the first trade the Kings made, they acquired the rights to future Hall-of-Famer Red Kelly from Toronto for defenseman Ken Block on June 8, 1967. Kelly had retired in 1967 but agreed to become the Kings' first head coach. The Maple Leafs insisted that Los Angeles should select Kelly in the 1967 NHL expansion draft. After LA failed to do so, Toronto wouldn't release his rights until the Kings traded for them.

2. The biggest trade in Kings' history and possibly all of hockey took place on August 9, 1988. Los Angeles acquired Wayne Gretzky, Marty McSorley and Mike Krushelnyski from Edmonton for forwards Jimmy Carson and Martin Gelinas plus 1st-round draft picks in 1989, 1991 and 1993, and cash. The draft picks were used on Jason Miller, Martin Ručinský, and Nick Stajduhar.

3. When the Kings traded Wayne Gretzky to St. Louis in February 1996, the deal didn't create nearly as many shock waves. The NHL's all-time leading scorer went to the Blues for Craig Johnson, Roman Vopat, Patrice Tardif, a 5th-round draft choice in 1996 and a 1st-round pick in 1997. Gretzky finished the season in St. Louis, then signed as a free agent with the New York Rangers shortly after.

4. Another blockbuster trade saw high-scoring center Bernie Nicholls head to the New York Rangers in January 1990

for forwards Tomas Sandström and Tony Granato. Nicholls had posted 758 points in 602 regular-season games before the deal and went on to score another 451 in his career. Sandström notched 254 points in 235 regular-season games as a King, while Granato tallied 305 points in 380 contests.

5. The Kings acquired center Marcel Dionne, the franchise's all-time leading scorer, in a trade with Detroit in June 1975. He arrived with Bart Crashley for forward Dan Maloney, defender Terry Harper and a 2nd-round draft choice in 1976. It remains one of the most one-sided trades in hockey history.

6. In 1986-87, Marcel Dionne was at odds with the franchise about the handling of coach Pat Quinn's contract and wanted the club to upgrade its roster or trade him to a Stanley Cup contender. He was then sent to the New York Rangers in March 1987 with Jeff Crossman and a 3rd-round draft choice for forward Bob Carpenter and defender Tom Laidlaw. Carpenter scored 83 points in 120 games before LA traded him, while Laidlaw played the final 195 games of his career with the team. Dionne scored 98 points in his final 118 career games with the Rangers.

7. LA dealt 1997-1998 Norris winner Rob Blake and rookie forward Steve Reinprecht to Colorado in February 2001 for Adam Deadmarsh, Aaron Miller, Jared Aulin and 1st-round draft picks in 2001 and 2003. Colorado won the Stanley Cup a few months after the trade. Blake posted 208

points in 322 regular-season games with Colorado, while Reinprecht scored another 353 NHL points. The players the Kings received combined for 136 points for the team. Blake returned to LA as a free agent in 2006 for two years before leaving for San Jose.

8. At the 1979-80 trade deadline, the Kings dealt center Butch Goring to the New York Islanders for forward Billy Harris and defender Dave Lewis. Goring was angry and disappointed. He had signed a six-year deal with LA a couple of years earlier and had posted 659 points in 736 regular-season games for the team. He then helped the Islanders win four straight Stanley Cups, scored 68 points in 99 playoff games, and won the 1980-81 Conn Smythe Trophy. Harris scored 60 points in 107 games with while Lewis tallied 41 points in 221 contests before LA traded them both.

9. Luc Robitaille was another Kings great who was traded by the club. He was shipped to Pittsburgh in July 1994 for power forward Rick Tocchet and a 2nd-round draft pick. After one season, he was traded by the Penguins to the New York Rangers. However, in August 1997, Kings general manager Dave Taylor reacquired Robitaille by sending Kevin Stevens to the Rangers. Robitaille then signed with Detroit as a free agent in July 2001 and returned to LA as a free agent two years later to finish his career.

10. One of the Kings' better deals resulted in the arrival of forward Jeff Carter from Columbus in February 2012 for

defenseman Jack Johnson and a 1st-round draft pick. By the end of 2019-20, Carter had 186 goals and 364 points in 540 games with LA. In addition, his 53 points in 73 playoff outings helped them capture two Stanley Cups. Johnson is a fine blue-liner who had 302 points at the end of 2019-20. Columbus used the draft pick on Marko Dano, who had 45 points in 145 games as of 2019-20.

CHAPTER 8:

DRAFT DAY

QUIZ TIME!

1. Which player did the Kings select 51st overall in 1969?

    a. Billy Smith
    b. Dale Hoganson
    c. Butch Goring
    d. Greg Boddy

2. How many defensemen did the club draft in 2008?

    a. 5
    b. 3
    c. 6
    d. 4

3. Rick Pagnutti was the Kings' first-ever draft pick and was selected 1st overall.

    a. True
    b. False

4. Who did the Kings select 11th overall in 2005?

    a. Jonathan Bernier
    b. Dustin Brown
    c. Anže Kopitar
    d. Jonathan Quick

5. In which round did the Kings take Rob Blake in the 1988 draft?

    a. 2nd
    b. 4th
    c. 1st
    d. 3rd

6. Of the 12 players LA drafted in 1980, how many appeared in at least 100 regular-season games?

    a. 8
    b. 5
    c. 9
    d. 7

7. Which star forward did the Kings draft 3rd overall in 1997?

    a. Mike Cammalleri
    b. Robert Lang
    c. Eric Belanger
    d. Olli Jokinen

8. Drew Doughty was selected 1st overall in 2008.

    a. True
    b. False

9. This defenseman was drafted 100th overall in 1983.

   a. Larry Murphy
   b. Dean Kennedy
   c. Garry Galley
   d. Craig Redmond

10. How deep in the draft did the Kings select Luc Robitaille?

    a. 171st overall
    b. 150th overall
    c. 191st overall
    d. 163rd overall

11. Dave Taylor was chosen in the 15th round of the 1975 draft.

    a. True
    b. False

12. Which player was drafted 5th overall in 2009?

    a. Tyler Toffoli
    b. Kyle Clifford
    c. Nick Shore
    d. Brayden Schenn

13. In what round did the Kings select Wayne Simmonds in 2007?

    a. 3rd
    b. 6th
    c. 4th
    d. 2nd

14. Jonathan Bernier is the highest-drafted goalie by the Kings as of 2019.

    a. True
    b. False

15. How many players have the Kings drafted 1st overall as of 2019?

    a. 2
    b. 3
    c. 1
    d. 4

16. Who did the Kings select 2nd overall in 1986?

    a. Mark Fitzpatrick
    b. Martin Gelinas
    c. Wayne McBean
    d. Jimmy Carson

17. This was the only player drafted by the Kings in 1979 who played over 1,000 NHL games.

    a. Jay Wells
    b. Mark Hardy
    c. Bernie Nicholls
    d. Tim Young

18. How many centers did the Kings select in the 2017 draft?

    a. 2
    b. 4
    c. 3
    d. 6

19. The Kings drafted this defenseman 118th overall in 2000.

    a. František Kaberle

    b. Mathieu Miron

    c. Ľubomír Višňovský

    d. Andreas Lilja

20. The lowest number of players the Kings have drafted in a year is three.

    a. True

    b. False

QUIZ ANSWERS

1. C – Butch Goring
2. D – 4
3. A – True
4. C – Anže Kopitar
5. B – 4th
6. D – 7
7. D – Olli Jokinen
8. B – False
9. C – Garry Galley
10. A – 171st overall
11. A – True
12. D – Brayden Schenn
13. D – 2nd
14. B – False
15. C – 1
16. D – Jimmy Carson
17. A – Jay Wells
18. C – 3
19. C – Ľubomír Višňovský
20. B – False

DID YOU KNOW?

1. After the 2019 NHL Draft was completed, the Kings had selected a total of 455 players since joining the league. They had selected first overall just once, had 11 picks in the top-5, and had chosen 19 players with a top-10 pick.

2. The first player ever taken by the club in the entry draft was also the only time the Kings have selected 1st overall, when they chose defenseman Rick Pagnutti in 1967. He never played a game in the NHL but tallied 229 points in 396 games in the minor leagues.

3. As of 2020, 15 former Kings' draft picks had played over 1,000 NHL games. They are Larry Murphy, Luc Robitaille, Darryl Sydor, Martin Gelinas, Rob Blake, Garry Galley, Bernie Nicholls, Dave Taylor, Butch Goring, Jay Wells, Olli Jokinen, Alexei Zhitnik, Dustin Brown, Anže Kopitar and Kimmo Timonen. In addition, four draft picks – Murphy, Billy Smith, Blake and Robitaille – have made it to the Hockey Hall of Fame.

4. The lowest-drafted King to play 1,000 NHL games was defenseman Kimmo Timonen, who was taken 250th overall in 1993. He notched 571 points in 1,108 regular-season games but never stepped on the ice for the Kings. Timonen remained in his native Finland after being drafted and was traded to Nashville in 1998 on the condition that Nashville wouldn't select Kings' defender Gary Galley in the 1998 NHL expansion draft.

5. In 1984, LA chose center Tom Glavine in the 4th round with the 69th overall pick. Glavine was also taken in the 2nd round of the Major League Baseball (MLB) draft by the Atlanta Braves. He probably made the right choice sticking with baseball since Glavine was a 10-time MLB All-Star who won a World Series, two Cy Young Awards, four Silver Slugger Awards, led the National League in wins five times, and was a World Series MVP.

6. As of 2019, the Kings had won the NHL draft lottery once. This allowed the club to move up in the draft order from 7th to 3rd overall in 1995. They then used the pick to take Aki Berg. The defenseman posted 43 points in 281 games with LA before being traded to Toronto. Berg left the NHL at the age of 27 and returned to Europe to continue his hockey career.

7. Larry Murphy finished his NHL career with four Stanley Cup rings and 1,217 points in 1,615 games with a +197 rating. The three-time All-Star also posted 115 assists in 215 playoff matches. The Kings drafted the blue-liner 4th overall in 1980 but traded him after 242-regular-season games in October 1983.

8. Another Hall-of-Famer drafted by the club who didn't last long in LA was goaltender Billy Smith, who was taken 59th overall in 1970. He played just five games with the Kings in 1971-72 and was then taken by the New York Islanders in the 1972 NHL expansion draft. Smith went on to win four Stanley Cups, the Vezina Trophy, the William M. Jennings Trophy and the Conn Smythe.

9. The highest-drafted goaltender by Los Angeles was Jamie Storr, who was selected 7th overall in 1994. He made his NHL debut in 1994-95, was named to the NHL's All-Rookie Team twice (1997-98 and 1998-99), and played with the club until 2003, when he signed as a free agent with Carolina. Storr went 85-78-21 in 205 regular-season games with LA while posting a 2.53 goals-against average and a .910 save percentage with 16 shutouts.

10. Winger Dave Taylor is currently the lowest-drafted player in NHL history to score 1,000 regular-season career points. He was taken in the 15th round with the 210th overall pick by LA in 1975 and went on to rack up 431 goals and 1,069 points in 1,111 games. He also added 59 points in 92 playoff games. Taylor played his entire NHL career in LA from 1977 to 1994.

CHAPTER 9:

GOALTENDER TIDBITS

QUIZ TIME!

1. Which goalie has played more regular-season games with the Kings?

    a. Kelly Hrudey

    b. Jonathan Quick

    c. Jamie Storr

    d. Rogatien Vachon

2. What was Wayne Rutledge's save percentage in the club's first season?

    a. .902

    b. .891

    c. .905

    d. .897

3. In 2017-18, Darcy Kuemper had a record of 10-1-3 in 19 games.

    a. True

    b. False

4. Which goalie recorded 14 losses in 2006-07?

   a. Mathieu Garon
   b. Sean Burke
   c. Dan Cloutier
   d. Yutaka Fukufuji

5. Who won 35 games in 1980-81?

   a. Mario Lessard
   b. Jim Rutherford
   c. Ron Grahame
   d. Doug Keans

6. This goaltender lost 29 of his 43 games played in 1969-70.

   a. Denis DeJordy
   b. Gerry Desjardins
   c. Wayne Rutledge
   d. Jack Norris

7. How old was Cristobal Huet when he made his NHL debut with the Kings?

   a. 19
   b. 23
   c. 27
   d. 30

8. Stéphane Fiset played a career-high 7 playoff games with the Kings.

   a. True
   b. False

9. How many games did Calvin Petersen start in 2018-19?

   a. 13

   b. 9

   c. 12

   d. 10

10. Which goalie played 28 games as a backup in 2008-09?

    a. Jean-Sébastian Aubin

    b. Jonathan Bernier

    c. Jason LaBarbera

    d. Erik Ersberg

11. As of 2019/20, 71 goalies have played at least one game for the Kings.

    a. True

    b. False

12. How many shots did Kelly Hrudey face in 1993-94?

    a. 1,955

    b. 2,184

    c. 1,927

    d. 2,219

13. Who had a goals-against average of 1.97 in 2013-14?

    a. Jonathan Bernier

    b. Jhonas Enroth

    c. Ben Scrivens

    d. Martin Jones

14. Jonathan Quick had a save percentage of 1.45 in the 2011-12 Stanley Cup playoffs.

   a. True
   b. False

15. Felix Potvin played how many regular-season games in 2001-02?

   a. 65
   b. 71
   c. 67
   d. 73

16. How many goals did Glenn Healy allow in the 1988-89 season?

   a. 192
   b. 164
   c. 147
   d. 119

17. Rogatien Vachon won how many games in the 1976-77 campaign?

   a. 26
   b. 29
   c. 10
   d. 33

18. How many goalies played at least 1 game in 2007-08?

   a. 4
   b. 5
   c. 6
   d. 7

19. Which goaltender recorded 66 career penalty minutes while playing for the Kings?

    a. Glenn Healy
    b. Bob Janecyk
    c. Kelly Hrudey
    d. Roland Melanson

20. Jonathan Quick has the most single-season shutouts by a Kings goaltender with 10.

    a. True
    b. False

QUIZ ANSWERS

1. B – Jonathan Quick

2. D – .897

3. A – True

4. C – Dan Cloutier

5. A – Mario Lessard

6. B – Gerry Desjardins

7. C – 27

8. A – True

9. D – 10

10. D – Erik Ersberg

11. A – True

12. D – 2,219

13. C – Ben Scrivens

14. B – False

15. B – 71

16. A – 192

17. D – 33

18. D – 7

19. C – Kelly Hrudey

20. A – True

DID YOU KNOW?

1. By the end of the 2019-20 season, the Kings had used 71 different goaltenders since making their NHL debut. Seven of these netminders played just one regular-season game with the club while 18 of them played in 10 or fewer.

2. One goaltender who played fewer than 10 games was Ben Bishop. He was acquired in a trade with Tampa in February 2017 and appeared in just 7 games over the remainder of the season. With Bishop set to become an unrestricted free agent, LA traded his rights to Dallas in May 2017. At 6-feet-7-inches, Bishop and Mikko Koskinen have been the tallest goalies ever to play in the NHL. Bishop, a two-time Second Team All-Star, led the NHL in goals-against average (2.06) in 2015-16 and save percentage (.934) in 2018-19.

3. Four former members of the Kings' goaltending fraternity are enshrined in the Hockey Hall of Fame in Toronto. They are Terry Sawchuk, Grant Fuhr, Rogatien Vachon and Billy Smith. However, Smith played just five regular-season games for the club, while Fuhr appeared in 14 and Sawchuk played 36.

4. Rogatien "Rogie" Vachon was one of the most popular Kings ever. He started his career with Montreal and even though he shared the 1967-68 Vézina Trophy, the Canadiens traded him to LA in November 1971. He played 389 games with the Kings and 25 in the playoffs before

signing as a free agent with Detroit in 1978. Vachon finished his career with a 353-293-128 record in 795 regular-season outings, with a 3.00 goals-against average, .896 save percentage and 51 shutouts. He later served as both coach and general manager of the Kings.

5. The Kings have used five goalies in a regular season on several occasions, but the most used in one campaign has been seven. That was in 2007-08 when Jason LaBarbera played in 45 games, Jean-Sébastian Aubin appeared in 19, Erik Ersberg played in 14, Dan Cloutier played in 9, Jonathan Bernier appeared in 4, Jonathan Quick in 3 and Danny Taylor played in 1.

6. Goaltender Yutaka Fukufuji was chosen with the 238th overall pick by LA in the 2004 draft and he became the first Japanese player to appear in an NHL contest. He was also the first Japanese goaltender and second Japanese citizen ever to be drafted. Fukufuji played in four games for the Kings in 2006-07 and close to 200 North American minor league contests until 2008-09.

7. The Kings drafted Cristobal Huet of France 214th overall in 2001, when he was 25 years old. He made his NHL debut in 2002-03 and played 53 games with the Kings until being traded to Montreal in June 2004. Huet was the first French goaltender to play in the NHL and became the first French-born player to win the Stanley Cup when he helped Chicago lift it in 2009-10.

8. Arguably the best goaltending the Kings ever received

came in the 2013-14 regular-season, when Jonathan Quick played in 49 games and Ben Scrivens and Martin Jones appeared in 19 each. They combined for team-bests in goals-against average at 1.99, save percentage at .923 and shutouts with 13. In addition, Quick won the William M. Jennings Trophy.

9. The most rambunctious Kings' netminder as of the conclusion of the 2019-20 campaign has been Kelly Hrudey. He was assessed a team-high 66 penalty minutes in his 360 regular-season games. He's followed closely by Jonathan Quick at 58 minutes, while Roland Melanson is next with 50 minutes, Bob Janecyk at 44 minutes and Glenn Healy with 34 minutes.

10. Although no goaltender has scored a goal while wearing a Kings' uniform, there have been several decent puck handlers in team history. Jonathan Quick had earned 19 assists by the end of 2019-20, while Kelly Hrudey finished his LA career with 8. Roland Melanson and Mario Lessard posted 6 each while Bob Janecyk, Felix Potvin and Mathieu Garon had 4 each.

CHAPTER 10:

ODDS & ENDS

QUIZ TIME!

1. When were the Kings placed in the Pacific Division?

    a. 1995-96

    b. 1990-91

    c. 1994-95

    d. 1993-94

2. Who scored the first hat trick in franchise history?

    a. Ted Irvine

    b. Eddie Joyal

    c. Lowell MacDonald

    d. Bill Flett

3. The Kings have had two mascots.

    a. True

    b. False

4. How many regular-season Kings games ended in a tie?

    a. 376

    b. 299

c. 424

d. 353

5. How many goals have the Kings scored on their 63 regular-season penalty shots?

    a. 20

    b. 24

    c. 21

    d. 26

6. Against what team did Wayne Gretzky score his legendary 802nd goal?

    a. Detroit Red Wings

    b. Vancouver Canucks

    c. Buffalo Sabres

    d. Quebec Nordiques

7. How many head coaches did the Kings have in 2011-12?

    a. 4

    b. 2

    c. 1

    d. 3

8. The Kings did not score on a penalty shot attempt until 1972.

    a. True

    b. False

9. As of 2020, the Kings' playoff record was?

    a. 111-144

    b. 112-143

c. 116-139

d. 109-146

10. The most overtime/shootout losses in a Kings' season is?

    a. 11

    b. 14

    c. 15

    d. 17

11. In 2016-17, the club lost more faceoffs than they won.

    a. True

    b. False

12. What was the final score of the Kings' first-ever victory?

    a. 5-3

    b. 5-0

    c. 4-1

    d. 4-2

13. How many skaters have played at least one game for the Kings as of 2019-20?

    a. 573

    b. 566

    c. 596

    d. 586

14. The Kings have attempted 5 penalty shots in playoff games as of 2020.

    a. True

    b. False

15. This was the first arena outside of California that the Kings played 100 games in.

    a. Joe Louis Arena (Detroit)
    b. Mellon Arena (Pittsburgh)
    c. Rexall Place (Edmonton)
    d. Scotiabank Saddledome (Calgary)

16. How many hits did the Kings register in 2009-10?

    a. 2,105
    b. 1,983
    c. 2,255
    d. 2,092

17. Who scored the Kings' first penalty shot goal?

    a. Butch Goring
    b. Juha Widing
    c. Ralph Backstrom
    d. Bob Pulford

18. How many games did the Kings play at the Los Angeles Memorial Sports Arena in 1967-68?

    a. 11
    b. 7
    c. 12
    d. 20

19. As of 2019-20, how many regular-season hat tricks have the Kings recorded?

    a. 176
    b. 199

c. 184

d. 195

20. Kingsley has been the team's mascot since 2007.

    a. True

    b. False

QUIZ ANSWERS

1. D – 1993-94

2. D – Bill Flett

3. A – True

4. C – 424

5. A – 20

6. B – Vancouver Canucks

7. D – 3

8. A – True

9. A – 111-144

10. C – 15

11. B – False

12. D – 4-2

13. C – 596

14. B – False

15. C – Rexall Place (Edmonton)

16. D – 2,092

17. A – Butch Goring

18. A – 11

19. C – 184

20. B – False

DID YOU KNOW?

1. The Kings have had 26 different head coaches in their history. Red Kelly was the first and Todd McLellan was the latest since 2019. Rogatien Vachon served three short stints in 1983-84, 1987-88, and 1994-95 on an emergency interim basis, while John Stevens had two stints in 2011 and 2017-18.

2. The longest-serving coach was Andy Murray, with 480 regular-season games, and he also earned the most points (520). Darryl Sutter won the most regular-season outings (225), coached the most postseason contests (69), recorded the most playoff victories (42), had the highest playoff winning percentage (.609), and the highest regular-season points percentage (.592). Rogatien Vachon coached the fewest regular-season games, with 10.

3. Forward Bob Pulford played for and coached the team as he played the final two seasons of his career in LA from 1970 to 1972. He tallied 30 goals and 80 points before hanging up his skates to take over as coach for five years. Pulford won the Jack Adams Award for 1974-75, when the team finished with a 42-17-21 record for 105 points.

4. Bob Pulford's son-in-law is Dean Lombardi, who was once the general manager and president of the Kings. Pulford left the organization in 1977 after feuding constantly with owner Jack Kent Cooke because Pulford also wanted to

serve as the general manager or have a larger role when it came to making player personnel decisions.

5. Six former Kings players went on to coach the team. They are Bob Pulford, Bob Berry, Rogatien Vachon, Mike Murphy and Larry Robinson. Former coaches Roger Neilson and Pat Quinn are in the Hockey Hall of Fame as builders while Bob Pulford, Red Kelly, and Larry Robinson are enshrined as players.

6. Eleven former Kings coaches never coached a playoff game for the club as of the end of the 2019-20 season. They are Hal Laycoe, Johnny Wilson, Fred Glover, Roger Neilson, Parker MacDonald, Larry Regan, John Torchetti, Marc Crawford, Rogatien Vachon, Willie Desjardins and Todd McLellan.

7. Since the team's inception, the Kings have had nine different general managers. Larry Regan was the first, followed by Jake Milford, George Maguire, Rogatien Vachon, Nick Beverley, Sam McMaster, Dave Taylor, Dean Lombardi and Rob Blake, who took over in 2017. Jake Milford is in the Hockey Hall of Fame as a builder.

8. Just one of the team's general managers failed to make the playoffs. That was Sam McMaster, who held the job from May 24, 1994 to April 22, 1997. Rogatien Vachon currently holds the mark for most playoff appearances (7), followed by Dean Lombardi (6) and George Maguire (5).

9. Dean Lombardi was the longest-serving general manager at 4,007 days. He took over on April 1, 2006, and left on

April 10, 2017. Both of the team's Stanley Cup victories came under Lombardi's watch. The shortest tenure was Nick Beverley's 692 days from June 15, 1992, to May 18, 1994.

10. Three sports broadcasters associated with the Kings have been honored with the Foster Hewitt Memorial Award for their contribution to hockey broadcasting. They are Jiggs McDonald in 1990, Bob Miller in 2000, and Nick Nickson in 2015. In addition, sportswriter Helene Elliott of the *Los Angeles Times* won the Elmer Ferguson Memorial

11. Award for her contributions to sports journalism.

CHAPTER 11:

KINGS ON THE BLUE LINE

QUIZ TIME!

1. Which defenseman had 100 penalty minutes and 38 points in the club's first season?

    a. Bill White

    b. Bob Wall

    c. Brent Hughes

    d. Dave Amadio

2. This defender had a team-low -15 rating in 2009-10.

    a. Alec Martinez

    b. Randy Jones

    c. Jack Johnson

    d. Davis Drewiske

3. Drew Doughty led the Kings in scoring in the 2011-12 playoffs.

    a. True

    b. False

4. How many blue-liners played a game for the Kings in the 1981-82 season?

    a. 9

    b. 15

    c. 12

    d. 10

5. Rob Blake earned how many assists in 1993-94?

    a. 43

    b. 13

    c. 7

    d. 48

6. Who recorded 119 penalty minutes in 1973-74?

    a. Bob Murdoch

    b. Sheldon Kannegiesser

    c. Barry Long

    d. Terry Harper

7. Which defenseman scored 4 power-play goals in 2016-17?

    a. Jake Muzzin

    b. Derek Forbort

    c. Drew Doughty

    d. Christian Folin

8. Marty McSorley was assessed 322 penalty minutes in 1988-89.

    a. True

    b. False

9. Who led Kings defensemen with 25 goals in 1988-89?

    a. Doug Crossman

    b. Steve Duchesne

    c. Dale DeGray

    d. Tim Watters

10. What was Drew Doughty's plus/minus rating in 2018-19?

    a. -23

    b. +10

    c. -34

    d. +14

11. Bob Murdoch earned 29 assists in 1975-76.

    a. True

    b. False

12. This defender was credited with 209 hits in the 2014-15 season.

    a. Matt Greene

    b. Robyn Regehr

    c. Brayden McNabb

    d. Jordan Nolan

13. How many points did Mark Hardy tally in 1984-85?

    a. 39

    b. 24

    c. 53

    d. 49

14. Bob Wall was the only defenseman to play all 74 games in the Kings' inaugural season.

a. True

b. False

15. Who blocked 128 shots in the 2013-14 regular season?

    a. Alec Martinez

    b. Jake Muzzin

    c. Robyn Regehr

    d. Willie Mitchell

16. Which defenseman scored 31 points in 1990-91?

    a. Steve Duchesne

    b. Bob Halkidis

    c. Todd Elik

    d. Brian Benning

17. Who was the only defenseman to score a game-winning goal in 1977-78?

    a. Gary Sargent

    b. Randy Manery

    c. Neil Komadoski

    d. Larry Brown

18. This defenseman led the Kings in scoring with 67 points in 2005-06.

    a. Mattias Norström

    b. Joe Corvo

    c. Ľubomír Višňovský

    d. Tim Gleason

19. Who scored 45 points to lead the Kings' defense in 1978-79?

a. Randy Manery

b. Robert Palmer

c. Rick Hampton

d. Darryl Edestrand

20. Charlie Huddy led the Kings in the 1992-93 playoffs with a +9 rating.

a. True

b. False

QUIZ ANSWERS

1. A – Bill White

2. C – Jack Johnson

3. B – False

4. C – 12

5. D – 48

6. D – Terry Harper

7. A – Jake Muzzin

8. B – False

9. B – Steve Duchesne

10. C – -34

11. A – True

12. A – Matt Greene

13. C – 53

14. B – False

15. D – Willie Mitchell

16. D – Brian Benning

17. A – Gary Sargent

18. C – Ľubomír Višňovský

19. B – Robert Palmer

20. A – True

DID YOU KNOW?

1. Five former Kings blue-liners have been inducted into the Hockey Hall of Fame. Those who have been honored so far are Rob Blake, Paul Coffey, Harry Howell, Larry Murphy and Larry Robinson. In addition, the Kings' first coach, Red Kelly, who excelled as both a defenseman and forward in the NHL, is also enshrined as a player.

2. When Jan Vopat patrolled the blue line for 65 games in the mid-1990s, he played with his brother Roman Vopat, a forward for the Kings. Jan notched 20 points and a +14 rating before being traded to Nashville in June 1998. Roman Vopat tallied 12 points in 54 games before being traded to Colorado in October 1998.

3. Jean Potvin, the brother of fellow blue-liner and Hall-of-Famer Denis Potvin, started his NHL career with LA in 1970-71 as a free agent. He played just 43 regular-season games and tallied 9 points before being involved in a multi-player trade with Philadelphia in January 1972. Jean and Denis' cousin Marc Potvin later played 23 games for the Kings in 1993 before being traded to Hartford. Sadly, Marc passed away in 2006 at the age of 38 while coaching in the United Hockey League.

4. The highest-scoring blue-liner in Kings' history is Drew Doughty. At the conclusion of the 2019-20 season, he had 117 goals and 502 points in 919 games and a +43 rating,

along with 51 points in 84 playoff contests. Doughty is a four-time All-Star who has won two Stanley Cups with the team and captured the Norris Trophy in 2015-16. His 919 games played was also a regular-season record for a Kings' defender.

5. The only other defender to win the Norris Trophy while playing with LA was Rob Blake in 1997-98. He tallied a club-high 161 goals for a defenseman and had 494 points in 805 regular-season contests, plus 24 points in 57 playoff outings. The Hall-of-Famer and four-time All-Star finished his career with 240 goals and 777 points in 1,270 regular-season games and was appointed general manager and vice president of the Kings on April 10, 2017.

6. Bob Murdoch was a steady defender who finished his Kings' career with a +80 rating to lead all blue-liners in that department. He was traded to LA by Montreal in May 1973 after winning two Stanley Cups with the Canadiens. Murdoch posted 171 points in 414 regular-season games with the Kings before being traded to Atlanta in January 1979. LA traded their 1974 first-round draft pick for Murdoch, which Montreal used to select Mario Tremblay.

7. Marty McSorley may be the all-time franchise leader in penalty minutes at 1,846, but he played forward as well as defense. Jay Wells racked up the most penalty minutes for a blue-liner and the third-most in Kings' history with 1,446 minutes in 604 games between 1980 and 1988. He also chipped in with 177 points and served another 110 minutes in 31 playoff games.

101

8. The 1966-67 Norris Trophy went to Harry Howell, who joined the Kings in February 1971, when he was traded by the California Golden Seals for cash. The Hall-of-Famer was 38 years old at the time and went on to tally 44 points in 168 games with LA before joining the World Hockey Association in 1973. He played three more seasons in the WHA before retiring at the age of 43.

9. Paul Coffey lived up to his name with the Kings because he basically stopped by for a cup of coffee from February 1992 to January 1993. He was acquired in a trade from Pittsburgh and chipped in with 62 points in 60 games and seven points in six playoff clashes. Coffey was then dealt to Detroit in a trade which saw LA reacquire high-scoring forward Jimmy Carson, who was included in the deal with Edmonton which brought Wayne Gretzky to LA.

10. Robert "Rob" Palmer was an underrated defender who was drafted 85th overall by LA in 1976. He led Kings blue-liners with 45 points in 1978-79 as a 22-year-old and posted another 40 points the next season. Palmer played 222 regular-season games with the team and contributed 94 points and a +12 rating before signing with New Jersey as a free agent in 1982.

CHAPTER 12:

CENTERS OF ATTENTION

QUIZ TIME!

1. How many points did Marcel Dionne rack up in 1979-80?

    a. 122

    b. 137

    c. 126

    d. 135

2. This center led the club with a +23 in 1999-00.

    a. Len Barrie

    b. Jason Blake

    c. Bryan Smolinski

    d. Jozef Stümpel

3. Anže Kopitar led the Kings with 51 assists in 2011-12.

    a. True

    b. False

4. This center has scored the most goals in a season as of 2019-20.

a. Wayne Gretzky

b. Marcel Dionne

c. Butch Goring

d. Bernie Nicholls

5. Who was the only player to score 2 shorthanded goals in 2017-18?

a. Nick Shore

b. Jussi Jokinen

c. Trevor Lewis

d. Tyler Toffoli

6. In how many seasons did Butch Goring score more than 50 points with LA?

a. 9

b. 8

c. 7

d. 6

7. How many points did Jimmy Carson notch as a rookie?

a. 79

b. 100

c. 39

d. 107

8. Derek Armstrong recorded the most hits on the team in 2007-08 with 311.

a. True

b. False

9. Who tallied 41 points in 46 games in 1991-92?

   a. Sylvain Couturier

   b. John McIntyre

   c. Randy Gilhen

   d. Corey Millen

10. In 1983-84, Doug Smith had a plus/minus rating of what?

   a. -22

   b. +13

   c. -32

   d. +7

11. Jarret Stoll had a face-off win percentage of 54.7 in 2013-14.

   a. True

   b. False

12. Which player recorded 112 penalty minutes in 1996-97?

   a. Dmitri Khristich

   b. Ray Ferraro

   c. Yanic Perreault

   d. Roman Vopat

13. How many goals did center/winger Mike Cammalleri score in 2005-06?

   a. 33

   b. 24

   c. 30

   d. 26

14. Marcel Dionne scored 19 power-play goals and 7 game-winning goals in 1978-79.

    a. True
    b. False

15. Which center did not play all 80 games in 1978-79?

    a. Vic Venasky
    b. Marcel Dionne
    c. Syl Apps
    d. Butch Goring

16. This center led the Kings with 74 points in 2001-02.

    a. Brad Chartrand
    b. Eric Belanger
    c. Jason Allison
    d. Bryan Smolinski

17. How many centers did the Kings use in the 1968-69 campaign?

    a. 5
    b. 8
    c. 6
    d. 7

18. How many faceoffs did Anže Kopitar win in 2018-19?

    a. 675
    b. 718
    c. 607
    d. 1,002

19. This player scored 10 goals in the 2013-14 playoffs.

   a. Jeff Carter

   b. Tyler Toffoli

   c. Anže Kopitar

   d. Mike Richards

20. Wayne Gretzky registered 47 points in the 1992-93 playoffs.

   a. True

   b. False

QUIZ ANSWERS

1. B – 137

2. D – Jozef Stümpel

3. A – True

4. D – Bernie Nicholls

5. C – Trevor Lewis

6. A – 9

7. A – 79

8. B – False

9. D – Corey Millen

10. C – -32

11. A – True

12. B – Ray Ferraro

13. D – 26

14. A – True

15. A – Vic Venasky

16. C – Jason Allison

17. D – 7

18. D – 1,002

19. A – Jeff Carter

20. B – False

DID YOU KNOW?

1. Wayne Gretzky and Marcel Dionne are currently the only former Kings centers who have been inducted into the Hockey Hall of Fame. Brian Kilrea, who played 25 games for the team in 1968, is also in the Hall in the builders category.

2. The NHL's all-time leading scorer with 894 goals and 2,857 points in 1,487 regular-season games, Wayne Gretzky contributed 246 goals and 672 assists for 918 points in 539 games with the Kings with 29 goals and 94 points in 60 playoff contests. He arrived to help turn the club's fortunes around in August 1988 in a massive trade with Edmonton. Gretzky led the Kings to the Stanley Cup Final in 1992-93 with 40 points in 24 playoff games but they lost to Montreal in five games.

3. Joining the Kings with Wayne Gretzky from the Oilers was Mike Krushelnyski, who played both center and wing during his career. He skated in 156 games with LA after the trade and chipped in with 109 points and a +23 rating. However, he was traded to Toronto in November 1990. His biggest goal for the Kings came in the 1990 playoffs when he scored in double overtime to eliminate the defending Stanley Cup champion Calgary Flames.

4. One of the players sent to Edmonton in the Wayne Gretzky trade was Jimmy Carson, who the Kings drafted

second overall in 1986. He had 92 goals and 186 points in 160 games with LA at the time of the deal. Carson then played with Edmonton and Detroit before the Kings reacquired him in a January 1993 trade with the Red Wings. He played another 59 games with 33 points before being swapped to Vancouver in January 1994.

5. The active leading scorer for the Kings is captain Anže Kopitar. The center was drafted 11th overall by the team in 2005 and has won two Stanley Cups, two Selke trophies and a Lady Byng Trophy with the squad. Kopitar had already played 1,073 regular-season NHL games by the end of 2019-20 with 333 goals, 950 points and a +76 rating. He also had 66 points in 79 postseason contests.

6. One of the earliest Kings' stars was Juha Widing. The Finnish center, who was known as "Whitey" and "The Flying Finn" by teammates and fans, posted five straight seasons with at least 55 points. He was acquired in a February 1970 trade with the New York Rangers and posted 342 points in 502 regular-season outings before being traded to the Cleveland Barons in January 1977. Sadly, Widing passed away at the age of 37 in 1984.

7. Jozef Stümpel was a dependable two-way center who arrived in Tinseltown from Boston in an August 1997 trade. He was traded back to Boston four years later and, believe it or not, swapped back to LA from Boston in June 2003. Stümpel then signed with Florida as a free agent in 2005. He skated in 334 regular-season games with the Kings and notched 267 points with a +48 rating.

8. After being drafted 47th overall by LA in 2010, Tyler Toffoli was a productive center who chipped in with 290 points in 515 contests and had an impressive +79 rating. He also notched 21 points in 47 playoff games and helped the Kings win the 2013-14 Stanley Cup. Toffoli led the league with 5 shorthanded goals in 2014-15 and with a +35 in 2015-16. He was traded to Vancouver in February 2020 for two players and two draft picks.

9. Sean Avery was a controversial agitator due to his on- and off-ice trash-talking and tactics. The Kings picked him up in 2003 trade with Detroit and he was dealt to the New York Rangers in February 2007. Avery led the league in penalty minutes with LA in 2003-04 and 2005-06 with 261 and 257 minutes, respectively. He registered 667 penalty minutes in 218 regular-season games with the Kings and contributed 99 points. Avery retired with 1,533 penalty minutes in 580 NHL outings.

10. Trevor Lewis has been an excellent depth player since making his debut with the Kings in 2008-09. He's averaged just 13:39 minutes of ice time by the end of 2019-20 and has contributed 163 points in 674 games with 23 points in 79 playoff clashes. Lewis has a knack for scoring big goals: 18 of his 70 regular-season markers (25.7 percent) have been game-winners. He's helped the Kings win two Stanley Cups and scored twice in the cup-winning game in 2012.

CHAPTER 13:

THE WINGERS TAKE FLIGHT

QUIZ TIME!

1. This winger led the Kings in penalty minutes in 2018-19 with 96.

    a. Kyle Clifford

    b. Dustin Brown

    c. Adrian Kempe

    d. Austin Wagner

2. Who scored 89 points in 68 games in 1990-91?

    a. Dave Taylor

    b. Tony Granato

    c. Tomas Sandström

    d. Luc Robitaille

3. Brian McLellan tallied 25 goals in 1983-84.

    a. True

    b. False

4. How many wingers played all 80 games in 1974-75?

    a. 2

    b. 4

    c. 3

    d. 5

5. Who scored 20 points in the Kings' 2011-12 Stanley Cup run?

    a. Mike Richards

    b. Dwight King

    c. Justin Williams

    d. Dustin Brown

6. Which right-winger scored 6 game-winning goals in 1967-68?

    a. Bill Flett

    b. Ted Irvine

    c. Howie Hughes

    d. Réal Lemieux

7. In 1997-98, this winger scored 52 points in 73 games.

    a. Craig Johnson

    b. Matt Johnson

    c. Vladimir Tsyplakov

    d. Glenn Murray

8. Bert Wilson led the team with 135 penalty minutes in 1977-78.

    a. True

    b. False

9. How many goals did Marian Gaborik score in the 2013-14 playoffs?

    a. 12

    b. 10

    c. 8

    d. 14

10. Who scored 7 power-play goals in 2005-06?

    a. Luc Robitaille

    b. Tom Kostopoulos

    c. Alex Frolov

    d. Pavol Demitra

11. Jari Kurri earned 60 assists in 1992-93.

    a. True

    b. False

12. Wayne Simmonds totaled how many hits in 2009-10?

    a. 143

    b. 189

    c. 155

    d. 123

13. How many points did Dave Taylor contribute in 1985-86?

    a. 87

    b. 71

    c. 49

    d. 94

14. Wayne Simmonds led the Kings in plus/minus rating in both the regular and postseason in 2009-10.

    a. True
    b. False

15. This winger led the Kings in goals in 2001-02.

    a. Ziggy Pálffy
    b. Adam Deadmarsh
    c. Steve Heinze
    d. Craig Johnson

16. Who took 226 shots on goal in 1969-70?

    a. Skip Krake
    b. Leon Rochefort
    c. Eddie Shack
    d. Ross Lonsberry

17. This winger won 67 faceoffs in only 25 games in 2016-17.

    a. Andy Andreoff
    b. Tanner Pearson
    c. Adrian Kempe
    d. Jarome Iginla

18. Alex Frolov scored how many goals in 2003-04?

    a. 24
    b. 27
    c. 22
    d. 30

19. Who was the only winger to play every regular-season game in 1980-81?

   a. Steve Jensen
   b. Greg Terrion
   c. Jim Fox
   d. Billy Harris

20. Charlie Simmer had the squad's lowest plus/minus rating in the 1979-80 season.

   a. True
   b. False

QUIZ ANSWERS

1. A – Kyle Clifford
2. C – Tomas Sandström
3. A – True
4. B – 4
5. D – Dustin Brown
6. A – Bill Flett
7. C – Vladimir Tsyplakov
8. B – False
9. D – 14
10. D – Pavol Demitra
11. A – True
12. D – 123
13. B – 71
14. A – True
15. A – Ziggy Pálffy
16. D – Ross Lonsberry
17. C – Adrian Kempe
18. A – 24
19. D – Billy Harris
20. B – False

DID YOU KNOW?

1. There are a half-dozen former Los Angeles Kings wingers enshrined in the Hockey Hall of Fame as of 2020. Jarome Iginla was the latest member of the fraternity to be inducted; he joins Steve Shutt, Jari Kurri, Dick Duff, Bob Pulford and Luc Robitaille.

2. Jari Kurri came to LA in a May 1991 trade with Philadelphia and banged in 108 goals and 293 points in 331 games before being traded to the New York Rangers in March 1996. Kurri finished his career with 601 goals, 1,398 points and a +304 rating in 1,251 games, along with 106 goals and 233 points in 200 postseason games. He also won five Stanley Cups, was named an All-Star five times and won the 1984-85 Lady Byng Trophy.

3. Despite being drafted 263rd overall by Pittsburgh in 2003, winger Matt Moulson has played 650 NHL games so far with 369 points to his name. Moulson kicked off his NHL career with the Kings after signing as a free agent in 2003. He made his big-league debut in 2007-08, the same season in which his brother-in-law, Jonathan Quick, played his first NHL game. Moulson notched 10 points in 29 games with LA before signing with the New York Islanders in 2009.

4. Another set of brothers-in-law who skated together with the Kings was made up of winger Tony Granato and

center Ray Ferraro. Granato arrived in LA in the blockbuster January 1990 trade that sent Bernie Nicholls to the New York Rangers. He posted 305 points in 380 games with the Kings and added 37 points in 52 playoff outings. Ferraro was also traded to LA from the Rangers, arriving in March 1996. He tallied 98 points in 197 contests before signing with Atlanta in 1999.

5. While playing for the Kings, Tony Granato received one of the longest suspensions in NHL history as he was banned for 15 games after slashing Chicago's Neil Wilkinson in the head in February 1994. Granato then received a serious head injury himself in January 1996, which required brain surgery and it was feared his career was over. However, he signed as a free agent with San Jose several months later, returned to the ice, and won the Bill Masterton Trophy for 1996-97.

6. The Kings also acquired winger Tomas Sandström in the Bernie Nicholls trade with the New York Rangers in January 1990. Sandström helped fill the void left by Nicholls' departure, as he scored 1.08 points-per-regular-season game with the club by notching 254 points in 235 outings with a +24 rating. He added 45 points in 50 playoff contests. Sandström was then traded to Pittsburgh in February 1994, when Marty McSorley was reacquired by LA.

7. Marty McSorley was originally acquired by the Kings in 1988 from Edmonton in the famous Wayne Gretzky trade.

He was considered by some to be Gretzky's personal bodyguard, as he racked up a franchise-high 1,846 penalty minutes and another 190 minutes in the postseason. McSorley played on the wing and blue line for the Kings and notched 234 points in 472 games. He led the league with a +48 in 1990-91 and with 399 penalty minutes in 1992-93.

8. The NHL's all-time penalty minute leader, Tiger Williams, also skated on the Kings' wing. He arrived in a trade with Detroit in March 1985 and stayed until October 1987, when he was sold to Hartford. He scored 40 goals and 90 points in 162 regular-season games, with 727 penalty minutes, and added 5 points and 34 penalty minutes in 8 playoff encounters. Williams finished his career with 241 goals and 513 points with 3,971 penalty minutes in 962 games. He also was assessed 455 penalty minutes in 83 playoff games.

9. Charlie Simmer skated on the famous "Triple Crown Line" with Marcel Dionne and fellow winger Dave Taylor. He posted 222 goals and 466 points in 384 regular-season games after signing as a free agent in 1977. Simmer's incredible 32.7 shooting percentage in 1980-81 is an NHL record and he led the league with 56 goals and 21 power-play goals in 1979-80 and in game-winners in 1980-81 with 10. He also topped the league in goals per game in 1979-80 and 1980-81, posting back-to-back 56-goal campaigns. Simmer was traded to Boston in October 1984 and won the Bill Masterton Trophy in 1985-86.

10. Žigmund "Ziggy" Pálffy spent 1999 to 2004 with the Kings and was very productive, with 150 goals, 340 points and a +85 rating in 311 contests, adding 19 points in 24 postseason games. Pálffy was acquired in a multi-player trade with the New York Islanders in June 1999 and remained until signing with Pittsburgh in 2005 for his final NHL season. Pálffy was a consistent scorer who finished in the NHL's top 10 three times for most goals, shorthanded goals and power-play goals in a season.

CHAPTER 14:

THE HEATED RIVALRIES

QUIZ TIME!

1. How many points have the Kings totaled in 257 regular-season games against the Vancouver Canucks?

    a. 244

    b. 256

    c. 232

    d. 260

2. Which team did the Kings defeat to win their first Stanley Cup?

    a. Chicago Blackhawks

    b. New Jersey Devils

    c. Boston Bruins

    d. Detroit Red Wings

3. The rivalry between the Kings and the California Golden Seals was known as "the Battle of California."

    a. True

    b. False

4. The Kings have lost how many games to the Calgary Flames in 247 regular-season meetings?

    a. 116
    b. 113
    c. 101
    d. 99

5. How many times did the Kings and San Jose Sharks meet in the playoffs between 2010 and 2016?

    a. 3
    b. 5
    c. 4
    d. 6

6. What was the score of the blowout win over Montreal on Dec. 10, 2013?

    a. 7-0
    b. 6-0
    c. 8-1
    d. 9-2

7. Which team did the Kings score 24 goals against over five games during the 1972-73 regular season?

    a. Philadelphia Flyers
    b. California Golden Seals
    c. Pittsburgh Penguins
    d. New York Islanders

8. The rivalry between the Kings and San Jose Sharks is known as the "Freeway Face-Off."

a. True

b. False

9. Who beat the Kings 10-3 on Feb. 13, 1993?

    a. Edmonton Oilers

    b. Chicago Blackhawks

    c. Washington Capitals

    d. Philadelphia Flyers

10. The Kings defeated this team in the 1992-93 conference finals.

    a. Toronto Maple Leafs

    b. Calgary Flames

    c. St. Louis Blues

    d. Edmonton Oilers

11. LA played their first-ever Stadium Series game against the Anaheim Ducks.

    a. True

    b. False

12. What team did the Kings play their first game against in Sweden as part of the 2011 NHL Premiere?

    a. Boston Bruins

    b. Colorado Avalanche

    c. Buffalo Sabres

    d. New York Rangers

13. How many goals has LA scored against San Jose in 157 regular-season games?

a. 455

b. 422

c. 443

d. 410

14. The Kings gave up 37 goals against the Minnesota North Stars in 1967-68.

a. True

b. False

15. Which team did the Kings lose all 8 regular-season games to in 2006-07?

a. San Jose Sharks

b. Anaheim Ducks

c. Dallas Stars

d. Phoenix Coyotes

16. What was the Kings' record after their first 13 games against the Vegas Golden Knights?

a. 7-5-1

b. 9-2-2

c. 8-4-1

d. 7-3-3

17. How many teams did the Kings go unbeaten against in the 2017-18 regular season?

a. 10

b. 11

c. 12

d. 13

18. What team did the Kings tie four games against in 1988-89?

    a. Detroit Red Wings
    b. Calgary Flames
    c. Edmonton Oilers
    d. Winnipeg Jets

19. How many goals did the Kings score against the Pittsburgh Penguins in 1967-68?

    a. 38
    b. 25
    c. 33
    d. 22

20. The Kings have tied 15 games with the Dallas Stars in 238 regular-season meetings.

    a. True
    b. False

QUIZ ANSWERS

1. D – 260

2. B – New Jersey Devils

3. A – True

4. A – 116

5. C – 4

6. B – 6-0

7. D – New York Islanders

8. B – False

9. C – Washington Capitals

10. A – Toronto Maple Leafs

11. A – True

12. D – New York Rangers

13. B – 422

14. A – True

15. C – Dallas Stars

16. C – 8-4-1

17. A – 10

18. D – Winnipeg Jets

19. C – 33

20. B – False

DID YOU KNOW?

1. With the Kings entering the NHL in 1967-68 with the Pittsburgh Penguins, St. Louis Blues, Minnesota North Stars, Oakland Seals and Philadelphia Flyers, there was a natural rivalry with the other five expansion clubs, especially the nearby Oakland Seals. Their regular-season won-lost-tied/overtime/shootout loss records against those teams at the conclusion of 2019-20 stood at: Pittsburgh 77-61-24; St Louis 78-103-26; Minnesota North Stars/Dallas Stars 89-107-42; Oakland Seals/Cleveland Barons 38-20-11; Philadelphia 48-86-17.

2. As of 2019-20, the current NHL teams the Kings have had the most regular-season success against when it comes to points percentage have been the Vegas Golden Knights (.654); Atlanta Thrashers/Winnipeg Jets (.629); Ottawa Senators (.628); Columbus Blue Jackets (.615) and New Jersey Devils (.603).

3. The current NHL squads that have been the most trouble for the Kings where regular-season points percentage is concerned are the Montreal Canadiens (.307); Boston Bruins (.358); Philadelphia Flyers (.374); Tampa Bay Lightning (.390) and St. Louis Blues (.440).

4. The Kings have developed intense rivalries with the two other NHL teams based in California, the Anaheim Ducks and the San Jose Sharks. Anaheim also plays in the Los

Angeles metropolitan area and their rivalry with the Kings is known as "the Freeway Face-Off" because the communities are separated by Interstate 5. The Kings eliminated both clubs during their 2013-14 Stanley Cup run and have also met them in the NHL Stadium Series outdoor games.

5. LA's regular-season record against Anaheim at the end of 2019-20 was 64-54-26 while their mark against San Jose was dead even at 68-68-21. The Kings won the only playoff series against Anaheim and have a 2-2 series postseason record against San Jose.

6. In the 2013-14 playoffs, Los Angeles lost the first three games of their Western Conference quarterfinal series against San Jose but came roaring back to win the series in seven games. The triumph meant the Kings were just the fourth team in NHL history to win a series after falling behind 3-0. In addition, Mike Richards and Jeff Carter became the first NHL players to achieve the feat twice, as they both played for Philadelphia in 2010 when the Flyers did the same thing.

7. The Kings have played a total of 49 playoff series as of 2020 with a record of 21-28 for a .429 winning percentage. LA had played 19 different teams in the postseason and had winning records against six of them, even records against three clubs and losing marks against the other 10 squads.

8. The team LA had faced most in the playoffs is the

Edmonton Oilers. They have met seven times and the Kings' record is just 2-5. The teams LA has met just once in the playoffs and beaten have been Arizona, Anaheim and New Jersey. The teams that have beaten LA in their only playoff meeting are the New York Islanders, Dallas Stars, Montreal Canadiens and Vegas Golden Knights.

9. "The Miracle on Manchester" was the name given to the Kings' historic comeback against Edmonton in the 1981-82 playoffs. LA won the first game 10-8 with Edmonton winning the second outing 3-2 in overtime to set the stage for Game 3 on April 10, 1982 at the Los Angeles Forum. Edmonton led 5-0 after two periods, but LA scored five straight goals in the third to tie the game, with the last goal coming with just five seconds remaining. Daryl Evans then scored at 2:35 of overtime to complete the biggest comeback in NHL history. LA went on to win the series 3-2.

10. The 1981-82 playoff series against Edmonton set several NHL records. The tilt produced a record 50 goals for a five-game series, a record the two teams broke in 1986 when they combined for 52 goals in 1986-87. The 18 goals scored in Game 1, which LA won 10-8, is a record for most goals in a playoff game. In addition, it was the biggest postseason series upset as Edmonton finished the regular season with 48 points more than the Kings.

CHAPTER 15:

THE AWARDS SECTION

QUIZ TIME!

1. Who was the first Kings player to appear in the NHL All-Star Game, in 1968?

   a. Eddie Joyal
   b. Terry Sawchuk
   c. Bill White
   d. Bill Flett

2. Who was the first coach of the Kings to win the Jack Adams Award?

   a. Bob Berry
   b. Pat Quinn
   c. Bob Pulford
   d. Tom Webster

3. Jimmy Carson was the only Kings player to be named to the NHL's All-Rookie Team.

   a. True
   b. False

4. How many times did Wayne Gretzky win the Art Ross Trophy in Los Angeles?

   a. 1
   b. 2
   c. 3
   d. 4

5. This player won the first Calder Memorial Trophy for the Kings.

   a. Dave Taylor
   b. Jonathan Quick
   c. Dustin Brown
   d. Luc Robitaille

6. Who won the Conn Smythe Trophy in the 2013-14 playoffs?

   a. Drew Doughty
   b. Justin Williams
   c. Anže Kopitar
   d. Jeff Carter

7. Who was the only member of the Kings to ever win the NHL Plus-Minus Award?

   a. Rob Blake
   b. Marcel Dionne
   c. Wayne Gretzky
   d. Marty McSorley

8. The team won its first division championship in 1990-91.

   a. True
   b. False

9. How many players from the Kings participated in the 1981 All-Star Game?

    a. 4
    b. 6
    c. 5
    d. 3

10. What year did Marcel Dionne win the Art Ross Trophy?

    a. 1977-78
    b. 1978-79
    c. 1980-81
    d. 1979-80

11. Drew Doughty won the James Norris Memorial Trophy in 2016-17.

    a. True
    b. False

12. How many times has Jonathan Quick won the William M. Jennings Trophy as of 2019-20?

    a. 3
    b. 1
    c. 2
    d. 0

13. This player won the Bill Masterton Memorial Trophy in 1977-78.

    a. Mike Murphy
    b. Butch Goring
    c. Syl Apps
    d. Pete Stemkowski

14. As of 2019-20, Wayne Gretzky is the only winner of the Hart Memorial Trophy for the Kings.

    a. True
    b. False

15. How many former Kings players have been inducted in the Hockey Hall of Fame player category as of 2020?

    a. 18
    b. 31
    c. 24
    d. 17

16. How many times has Anže Kopitar won the team's Leading Scorer Award?

    a. 10
    b. 11
    c. 9
    d. 12

17. Which award did Dustin Brown receive in 2010-11?

    a. NHL Foundation Player Award
    b. Mark Messier Leadership Award
    c. Lester Patrick Trophy
    d. Frank J. Selke Trophy

18. Who won the Frank J. Selke Trophy in 2017-18?

    a. Mike Cammalleri
    b. Marian Gaborik
    c. Anže Kopitar
    d. Tanner Pearson

19. Who was the first Kings goalie to make the NHL All-Rookie Team?

    a. Jonathan Quick
    b. Jack Campbell
    c. Jonathan Bernier
    d. Jamie Storr

20. Marcel Dionne won the Lady Byng Memorial Trophy in back-to-back seasons with the Kings.

    a. True
    b. False

QUIZ ANSWERS

1. B – Terry Sawchuk

2. C – Bob Pulford

3. B – False

4. C – 3

5. D – Luc Robitaille

6. B – Justin Williams

7. D – Marty McSorley

8. A – True

9. A – 4

10. D – 1979-80

11. B – False

12. C – 2

13. B – Butch Goring

14. A – True

15. D – 17

16. D – 12

17. A – NHL Foundation Player Award

18. C – Anže Kopitar

19. D – Jamie Storr

20. B – False

DID YOU KNOW?

1. As a franchise, the Kings have won numerous team and individual NHL awards as of 2019. They include Stanley Cup (2), Clarence S. Campbell Bowl (3), Art Ross Trophy (4), Bill Masterton Memorial Trophy (3), Calder Memorial Trophy (1), Conn Smythe Trophy (2), Frank J. Selke Trophy (2), Hart Memorial Trophy (1), Jack Adams Award (1), James Norris Memorial Trophy (2), King Clancy Memorial Trophy (1), Lady Byng Memorial Trophy (6), Ted Lindsay Award (2) and William M. Jennings Trophy (2).

2. The Kings have yet to win a President's Trophy for leading the league in points during the regular season. In addition, no player has won the Vézina Trophy as the league's top goaltender in the regular season or the Rocket Richard Trophy for leading the NHL in goals during the regular season.

3. Those who have led the NHL in scoring while playing for the Kings are centers Marcel Dionne and Wayne Gretzky. Dionne won the award in 1979-80 while Gretzky took it home for 1989-90, 1990-91, and 1993-94.

4. Since 1982, the team allowing the fewest regular-season goals has been rewarded with the William M. Jennings Award. This silverware was won by Jonathan Quick for his performances in 2013-14 and 2017-18.

5. The Bill Masterton Trophy is awarded annually to the player who exemplifies perseverance, sportsmanship and dedication to hockey. Butch Goring won it in 1977-78, while fellow center Bob Bourne was honored a decade later in 1987-88. Winger Dave Taylor won it in 1990-91.

6. The most valuable player in the playoffs is rewarded with the Conn Smythe Trophy. The Kings to win this trophy are goaltender Jonathan Quick in 2011-12 and forward Justin Williams for 2013-14. The team won the Stanley Cup both those seasons.

7. The Hart Memorial Trophy is awarded to the player deemed most valuable to his team during the regular season and is voted on by the media. The NHL Players' Association also takes its own vote and gives the season MVP the Ted Lindsay Award. Marcel Dionne won the Ted Lindsay Award in 1978-79 and 1979-80 while Wayne Gretzky won the Hart Trophy in 1988-89.

8. The NHL player who best exhibits sportsmanship and gentlemanly conduct receives the Lady Byng Trophy each year. The trophy has been won by four Kings centers. Marcel Dionne was the winner for 1976-77; Butch Goring won it the following year; Wayne Gretzky won in 1990-91, 1991-92 and 1993-94; and Anže Kopitar won in 2015-16.

9. Anže Kopitar won the Frank J. Selke Trophy as the league's best defensive forward in 2015-16 and 2017-18. Rob Blake won the James Norris Trophy as the best defenseman in the league for 1997-98 and Drew Doughty

followed suit in 2015-16. In addition, winger Luc Robitaille was named the rookie of the year for 1986-87 and won the Calder Trophy.

10. As for the end-of-season All-Star Teams, Kings players who have been chosen at least once for the first or second teams are goaltenders Rogatien Vachon, Mario Lessard and Jonathan Quick; defenders Rob Blake and Drew Doughty; left-wingers Luc Robitaille and Charlie Simmer; centers Marcel Dionne and Wayne Gretzky; and right-winger Dave Taylor.

CONCLUSION

The Los Angeles Kings have been thrilling California hockey fans for over half a century now. And, even though the club has recently suffered a low point in its history, it's bound to bounce back in the near future.

The trivia/fact book you've just read deals with the franchise's history from the very beginning right to the final day of the NHL's 2019-20 regular season. Included are trivia questions, facts and anecdotes about your favorite Los Angeles players, coaches, general managers, etc.

Our aim is to entertain Kings fans in a lighthearted and fun manner with the book so they can relive the highs and lows of this great organization. We also hope you may have learned something you may not have known while reading through it.

With a pair of Stanley Cups under their belt, the Kings have been a successful franchise since joining the league in the 1967 expansion. The team quickly became accustomed to the Staples Center after playing the first few decades at the Los Angeles Forum.

You'll be able to prepare yourself with the information needed to challenge family, friends and fellow fans in trivia contests with this book, and you may be able to convert some along the way.

Los Angeles Kings fans are already among the most knowledgeable in the league and have stuck with their team through thick and thin. We hope this book can be a help to you when it comes time to show who the boss it when it comes to Kings' trivia.

Thanks for supporting the team and taking the time and effort to read through the organization's newest trivia/fact book.

Made in the USA
Monee, IL
29 November 2020

50078844R00085